NATIONAL CURRICULUM E

UNDERSTANDING
MATHEMATICS

Second Edition

2

C. J. Cox & D. Bell

JOHN MURRAY

© C. J. Cox and D. Bell, 1985, 1989

First published in 1985
by John Murray (Publishers) Ltd
50 Albemarle Street, London W1X 4BD

Reprinted 1985, 1987

Second edition 1989

Reprinted 1991, 1993, 1994, 1995

Printed in Great Britain at the Alden Press, Oxford

A CIP catalogue record for this book is available from the British Library

ISBN 0–7195–4754–7

Preface

Understanding Mathematics is a complete course of five books for secondary pupils in the 11–16 age range. This is the second of a three-book course covering Key Stage 3 of the National Curriculum Programme to Level 8. The parallel series, **Steps in Understanding Mathematics**, covers up to Level 6 with some extension to Level 7.

The development of each topic was planned with reference to the findings of the research project *Concepts in Secondary Mathematics and Science* (CSMS), resulting in 'common core' exercises with a less steep incline of difficulty than other texts. In both series, pupils are stretched by extension (boxed) activities, while the common core allows easy transfer between sets, and between the two series. The emphasis on constant revision within the exercises (an approach that is echoed in the National Mathematics Curriculum), together with the Summaries, the Glossary, and the weekly revision Papers, has proved a very successful confidence-building approach.

The **Teachers' Resource Books** have teaching notes and demonstration examples; transparency masters; answers, including diagrams; aural (mental) tests; practical worksheet masters; assessment tests; computer teaching programs.

Two further publications supplement the main course: **Aural Tests in Mathematics** (Books 1–5) provide essential practice in life-skills, and **Mathematics Coursework 1–3** encourages pupils to explore mathematical ideas – to say 'What if ...?'

Notes on this National Curriculum edition

It is possible to use this edition alongside the first edition. The only major change is the replacement of chapter 19 on bases (now a project on binary in Book 1) with a chapter on ratio and proportion, originally Book 1, chapter 12. Minor changes include:

chapter 4 includes examples of Carroll diagrams;

chapter 13 includes a map to aid teaching of grid references;

chapters 12 and 21 introduce calculator solution ('trial and improvement');

chapter 28 has been shortened to allow a new project introducing decision trees for identification;

chapter 34 includes congruent as well as similar shapes.

Acknowledgements

The authors have been delighted with the enthusiastic reception given to the Understanding Mathematics series and wish to thank their publishers, reviewers, and all who have written with encouraging comments and helpful suggestions, especially the Devon Users Group, and the pupils and teachers who have written (from as far away as Kuwait!) in response to the 'challenges'.

We are also grateful for advice given during preparation of the first edition from:

Kath Hart, Brian Bolt (Exeter University), Andrew Rothery (Worcester College of Education), Alec Penfold, Martyn Dunford (Huish Episcopi School), Jacqueline Gilday (Wells Blue School), Hazel Bevan (Millfield School), John Wishlade (Uffculme School), John Halsall, David Symes, Simon Goodenough, Mary Mears.

Thanks are also due to the editorial and production staff at John Murray, the illustrator Tony Langham, and to all the many teachers and pupils who have helped in the testing and revising of the course.

Photographs by permission of: Rob Matheson/ZEFA (p. 59); Sinclair Research (p. 94); Spanish National Tourist Office (p. 139); Swiss National Tourist Office and Swiss Federal Railways (p. 130); Sealink U.K. Ltd (p. 142).

New **diagrams** by Technical Art Services.

New **cartoons** by Impress International.

Contents

About this book

This is the second book of **Understanding Mathematics**, a course leading to GCSE Mathematics and National Assessment after Key Stages 3 and 4.

Each chapter is concerned with a mathematical topic, and is divided into **exercises**. **New ideas** are clearly explained, and **discussion starters** give you the chance to talk about the mathematics and to see how it links with everyday life. **Computer programs** are included; the BASIC used will work on all the popular micros.

Almost all the exercises have four kinds of question:

- **Introductory questions** are for everyone.
- **Starred questions** are optional for those who find the introductory questions very easy.
- **Further questions** follow. These continue the topic to a higher level.
- **Boxed question** challenge those who are keen and quick, and give lots of ideas for investigations and practical work.

This structure helps you learn at your own pace, and builds up your confidence.

The book also includes:

- **Using your calculator** exercises
- **Projects**
- **Papers** – for homework and revision
- **Summaries** of the ideas met in each chapter, to help you study and revise.
- **Glossary,** giving the meaning of mathematical words which you will meet in the course.

Your teacher will also give you **worksheets** during the course for projects, practical work and assessment.

1 Angles and scales: journeys

A Cardinal points; clock bearings

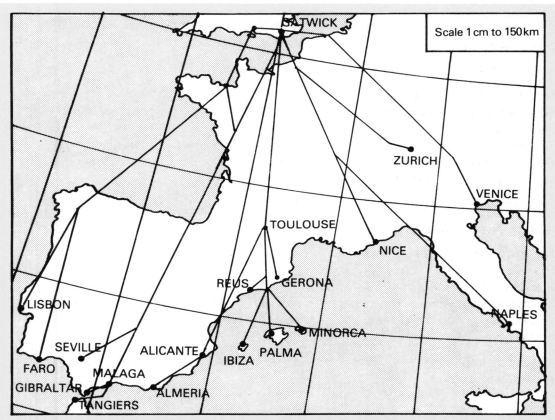

Fig. 1:1

Example

X————————————————————Y

Fig. 1:2

Line XY is 5.7 cm long.

If it is drawn to a scale of:	The true distance of X from Y is:
(i) 1 cm to 2 km	5.7 × 2 km = 11.4 km
(ii) 1 cm to 500 m	5.7 × 500 m = 2850 m = 2.85 km
(iii) 1 cm to 50 km	5.7 × 50 km = 285 km

For Discussion

Set A

Scales: (a) 1 cm to 2 km
       (b) 1 cm to 500 m

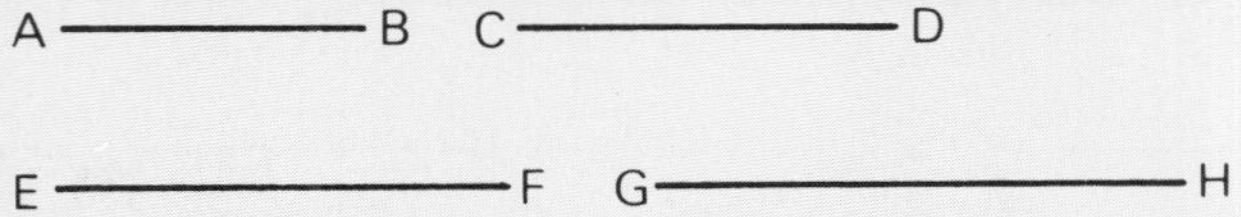

A ————————— B   C ———————————— D

E ————————————— F   G —————————————————— H

Fig. 1:3

Set B

Scales: (c) 1 cm to 50 km
       (d) 1 cm to 20 km

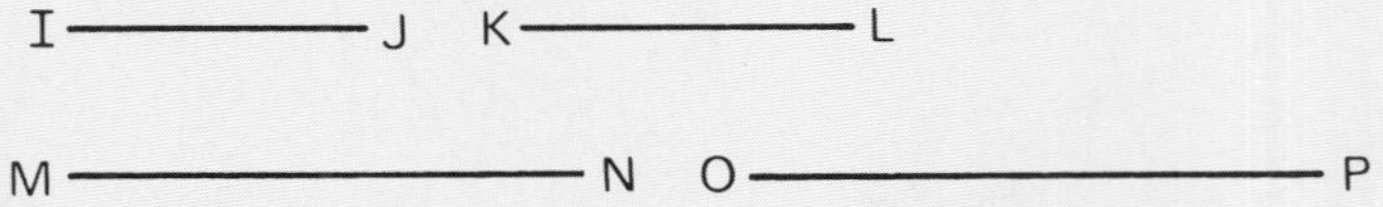

I ——————— J   K ——————— L

M ————————————— N   O ————————————— P

Fig. 1:4

1 Figure 1:5 shows a 16-cardinal-point compass. Copy Figure 1:6, which is a simplified version of the compass.

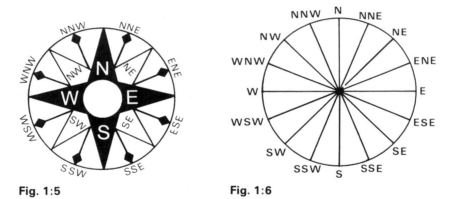

Fig. 1:5   **Fig. 1:6**

2 How many degrees, measured clockwise, between:
(a) N and E   (b) N and W   (c) S and E   (d) NE and SE
(e) SE and NW   (f) N and SW   (g) S and NE?

3 For each of the following state which way you will be facing if you start looking in the given direction, then turn clockwise through the given number of degrees.
(a) (N, 180°)   (b) (W, 270°)   (c) (NE, 90°)   (d) (SE, 135°)   (e) (SE, 225°)
(f) (SW, 315°)

4 State the clock bearings of the dots on the objects in Figure 1:7, assuming you are standing at the centre of the clock face and take the steeple as being at 12 o'clock.

Example   The foot of the tree is at 2 o'clock.

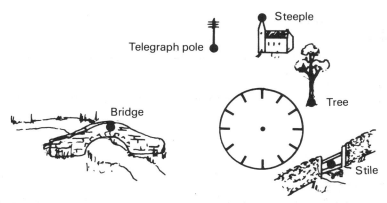

Fig. 1:7

*5 How many degrees, measured clockwise, between:
(a) N and S   (b) S and W   (c) W and E   (d) W and NW   (e) NE and E
(f) SW and W   (g) W and NE   (h) N and SE   (i) SE and W
(j) SW and SE?

*6 Draw a clock as in Figure 1:7, then draw a picture of:
(a) a steeple at 12 o'clock   (b) a telegraph pole at 6 o'clock
(c) a tree at 9 o'clock   (d) a man at 4 o'clock   (e) a car at 10 o'clock.

*7 Design your own clock-bearing picture. State which object is at 12 o'clock and at what o'clock the other objects are.

8 Repeat question 3 for the following turns.
(a) (N, $22\frac{1}{2}°$)   (b) (N, $337\frac{1}{2}°$)   (c) (NE, $202\frac{1}{2}°$)   (d) (SSW, 90°)
(e) (NNW, 45°)   (f) (NNE, 135°)   (g) (NNW, $292\frac{1}{2}°$)   (h) (SSW, $22\frac{1}{2}°$)
(i) (ENE, $157\frac{1}{2}°$)   (j) (WSW, $382\frac{1}{2}°$)

9 Repeat question 4 if the bridge is taken as 12 o'clock.

10 If Figure 1:7 is drawn to a scale of 1 cm to 500 m, how far from the centre of the clock, both in metres and in kilometres, is the dot on each object?

11 In Figure 1:8 the scale is 1 cm represents 2 km.

(a) How far is B from A in km?

(b) If you were standing at A, the point B would be NE of you. If you were standing at B, what would be the bearing of A?

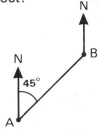

Fig. 1:8

12 Using a scale of 1 cm to 2 km, draw a diagram to show:
(a) D, NW of C; 6 km away   (b) G, SE of F; 5 km away
(c) I, NE of H; 4 km away   (d) K, SW of J; 5 km away.

13 In the diagrams you drew for question 12 what is the cardinal (NSWE) bearing of:
(a) C from D   (b) F from G   (c) H from I   (d) J from K?

14 Figure 1:9 shows the track of an aeroplane to a scale of 1 cm to 50 km.

The plane flies due north for 100 km, then SE for 80 km.

How far is C from A, to the nearest 10 km?

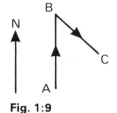

Fig. 1:9

15 Figure 1:10 shows some journeys drawn to a scale of 1 cm to 50 km. Describe each journey with a sentence like the one in italics in question 14.

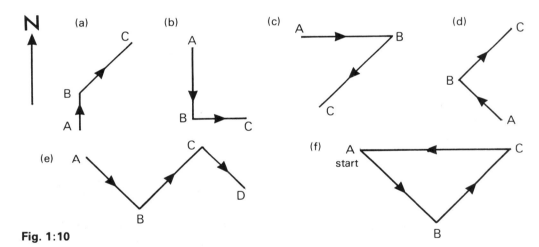

Fig. 1:10

16 Copy exactly the diagrams in Figure 1:10, but turn the arrows the other way. Write descriptions of the new journeys, giving distances to the nearest 4 km if the scale is changed to 1 cm represents 20 km.

17 An aircraft pilot receives signals from two beacons, A and B. On his map, B is marked as being 4 km due east of A. He can tell by the signals that B is due north of him and A is north-west of him. Draw a scale diagram to find his position relative to A and B, stating how far he is from each.

18 Draw a compass like the one in Figure 1:5.

19 Figure 1:11 shows how to find north using a watch set to GMT. First line up the hour hand with the sun (pointing *away* from it). Then bisect the angle between the hour hand and 12 to give north.

Draw pictures of watch faces to show the position of the sun and north at 10 a.m. and at 1700 hours.

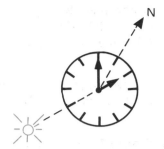

Fig. 1:11

20 Figure 1:12 shows the North Star (Polaris), which is directly above the North Pole. Polaris is always in the north and the other stars appear to rotate round it. Why?

Find Polaris on the next starry night.

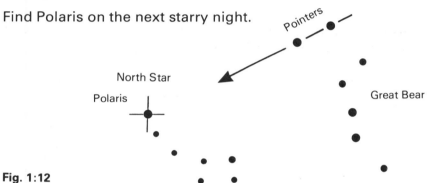

Fig. 1:12

B 3-figure bearings; scale journeys

Example Draw a scale plan of a journey that starts on a bearing of 135° for 1 km, then changes to 270° for ½ km. Use a scale of 4 cm represents 1 km.

Answer:

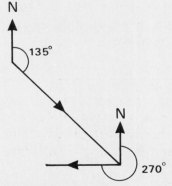

Scale 4 cm rep. 1 km

Fig. 1:13

For Discussion

Draw a scale plan of the following journey, using a scale of 1 cm to 100 km. You will need to leave a 2 cm space above the starting point, 4 cm below it, and 8 cm on the right.

Start on a bearing of 105°. After 550 km, turn to 140° for 250 km. Then head on 000° for 200 km before turning to 305° for the last 150 km.

How far is it in a straight line from the start to the finish, to the nearest 50 km?

1 In Figure 1:14, the compass needle points north. A is on a bearing of 070°. State the bearings of points B to M, in alphabetical order.

2 In Figure 1:14, B is east or 090°. Give, both as a cardinal bearing and as a 3-figure bearing, the positions of points C to G (*not* H to M).

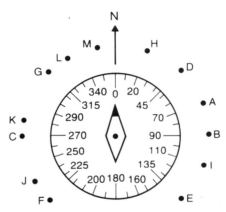

Fig. 1:14

3 Copy Figure 1:15, leaving a 5 cm space all round O. Then mark the following points on the given bearings, each point being 5 cm from O.

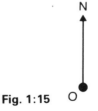

   (a) A, 020°   (b) B, 110°   (c) C, 200°
   (d) D, 240°   (e) E, 300°   (f) F, 330°   **Fig. 1:15** O

4 Look back to Figure 1:9. Using 3-figure bearings we could describe the journey as *'Start on 000°, then turn to 135°.'*

Write a sentence like the one in italics to describe each journey in Figure 1:10. Note that all sloping lines are at 45° to the vertical.

*5 Copy the compass in Figure 1:14, making the circle of radius 5 cm, but do not copy points A to M. Mark instead the following points.
   (a) (N, 000°)   (b) (O, 030°)   (c) (P, 080°)   (d) (Q, 110°)   (e) (R, 160°)
   (f) (S, 180°)   (g) (T, 200°)   (h) (U, 225°)   (i) (V, 250°)   (j) (W, 270°)
   (k) (X, 300°)   (l) (Y, 315°)   (m) (Z, 350°)

*6   Using a protractor and a ruler, copy the diagrams in Figure 1:10, but reverse the direction of each arrow.

Write a sentence about the bearings in each journey.

Example   (a)

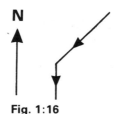

Fig. 1:16

Start on 225°, then change to 180°.

*7   Draw a plan of the following to a scale of 4 cm represents 1 km. Each turn is to be made after 1 km, and the whole journey is to be $1\frac{1}{2}$ km. For an example see the beginning of this exercise.

(a) Start on 090°, then change to 180°.   (b) Start on 180°, then change to 090°.

(c) Start on 135°, then change to 090°.   (d) Start on 090°, then change to 135°.

(e) Start on 135°, then change to 000°.   (f) Start on 135°, then change to 045°.

8   On squared paper (5 mm or 6 mm is best) draw two sets of axes from 0 to 10 each. Plot the following two journeys, all lines between turning points being straight. Use arrows to show the direction of travel.

(a) Start at (0,0). Go to (5,6), then to (10,0), then (10,4), then (5,9), then (0,4), and finally back to (0,0).

(b) Start at (0,0). Go to (5,3), then to (0,9), then (3,9), then (10,4), then (3,0), and finally back to (0,0).

9   For each journey in question 8 give the 3-figure bearings (to the nearest 5°) taken at each turn.

Start: (a) 040°; 140°; 000°; . . .

10 The journey in Figure 1:17 starts at A. It can be described as: *Bearing 050° for 100 km, then 300° for 120 km.*

Describe the journeys in Figure 1:18 with a sentence like the one in italics. Note that the diagrams are not drawn accurately, so you must calculate, not measure, the bearings.

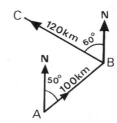

Fig. 1:17

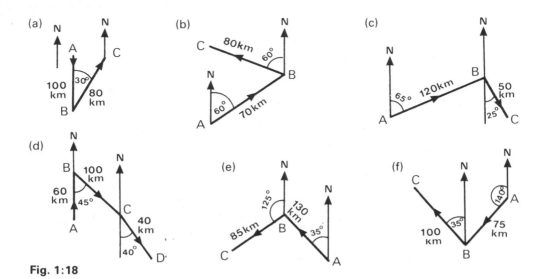

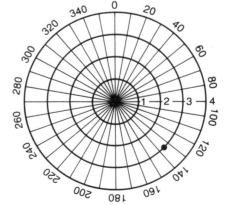

Fig. 1:18

11 Draw the following journeys, using a scale of 1 cm to 100 km. You will need a 6 cm space to the right of each starting point and a 6 cm space below it. Remember to construct an accurate north line at each turning point.

(a) 400 km on 150°, then 300 km on 050°, then 150 km on 290°.

(b) 400 km on 170°, then 250 km on 110°, then 450 km on 035°, then 400 km on 260°.

Measure to find the shortest distance of each start from each finish, correct to the nearest 50 km.

---

12 Figure 1:19 represents a radar screen. Draw an enlarged copy of it. The circles are to be spaced every 1.5 cm and represent kilometres. An object 3 km from the radar aerial on a bearing of 135° is marked with a dot. We could say it is at (3, 135°).

Mark on your screen:

A: (3, 040°);   B: (2, 120°);   C: (4, 200°);
D: (3, 215°);   E: (3, 245°);   F: (2, 305°);
G: (2½, 270°);   H: (3½, 335°);   I: (2¼, 335°).

Fig. 1:19

13 Draw an island with some important features marked, including a radar station. List the radar bearing of each feature.

2 Algebra: powers

A Powers of one letter

w^2 **is the shorthand way of writing** $w \times w$.

Be careful not to confuse it with $2w$, which is the shorthand for $2 \times w$ or $w + w$.

$2w^2$ **is shorthand for** $2 \times w^2$.

Examples If $h = 5$ then $h^2 = 5 \times 5 = 25$ and $h^3 = 5 \times 5 \times 5 = 125$.

If $b = 2$ then $b^2 = 4$ and $2b^2 = 8$.
Note that you must square the b before you multiply by the 2.

1 Write the shorthand for:
(a) $w \times w$ (b) $w + w$ (c) $k \times k \times k \times k$ (d) $3 \times a$ (e) $2 \times b \times b$
(f) $2 \times m \times m \times m$ (g) $a + a + a$.

2 Write in full, as in question 1:
(a) a^2 (b) $2a$ (two ways)   (c) a^3 (d) $3a$ (two ways)   (e) $2a^2$ (f) $3a^3$.

3 If $s = 2$ and $t = 1$ find the value of:
(a) s^2 (b) s^3 (c) s^4 (d) t^2 (e) t^3.

4 Find the value of $2a^2$ if a is:
(a) 2   (b) 3   (c) 1   (d) 0   (e) 4.

*5 If $a = 1$, $b = 2$ and $c = 3$ find the value of:
(a) a^2 (b) b^2 (c) c^2 (d) a^3 (e) b^3 (f) c^3 (g) $2a^2$
(h) $2b^2$ (i) $2c^2$.

6 If $w = 1$, $x = 3$, $y = 4$ and $z = 0$ find the value of:
(a) w^3 (b) x^3 (c) y^3 (d) z^2 (e) $3w^2$ (f) $3x^2$ (g) $4z^3$.

7 Find the value of:
(a) $2a^2$ if $a = 2$ (b) $3b^2$ if $b = 1$ (c) $9c^2$ if $c = 3$ (d) $2d^3$ if $d = 2$
(e) $2e^4$ if $e = 1$ (f) f^{100} if $f = 1$.

8 **Example** $2a^2 = 2 \times a^2 = 2 \times a \times a$ **but** $(2a)^2 = 2a \times 2a = 2 \times a \times 2 \times a$.

If $a = 3$: $2a^2 = 2 \times 3 \times 3 = 18$ **but** $(2a)^2 = 6 \times 6 = 36$.

Find the values of:
(a) $3a^2$ and $(3a)^2$ if $a = 2$ (b) $5c^2$ and $(5c)^2$ if $c = 5$ (c) $2d^2$ and $(2d)^2$ if $d = 1.5$
(d) $4e^2$ and $(4e)^2$ if $e = 0.3$

9 Find the values of $\frac{n^2}{4}$ and $\left(\frac{n}{4}\right)^2$ if:

(a) $n = 4$ (b) $n = 8$ (c) $n = 12$.

10 Examples $12 = 2 \times 6 = 2 \times 2 \times 3$

$16 = 2 \times 8 = 2 \times 2 \times 4 = 2 \times 2 \times 2 \times 2$

Split up into prime factors as in the examples:
(a) 8   (b) 9   (c) 15   (d) 20   (e) 24   (f) 30   (g) 36
(h) 27   (i) 50   (j) 49   (k) 48.

11 From the examples in question 10, $12 = 2^2 \times 3$ and $16 = 2^4$.

Write your answers to question 10 using indices.

B   Powers of more than one letter

```
10 PRINT "What number is p?"
20 INPUT P
30 PRINT "What number is q?"
40 INPUT Q
50 PRINT "The value of 2*p↑2*q is ‸";2*P*P*Q
```

Every computer program uses letters to stand for numbers. By changing line 50 you could find the value of any expression containing p and q. The computer does not understand the meaning of pq. You must tell it to work out $p \times q$, written as P*Q.

Note that $p↑2$ is the way that you write p^2 on the screen.

1 Example $t \times t \times t + 3 \times t \times t \equiv t^3 + 3t^2$. (The sign $\equiv$ means 'is identical to'.)

Write in shorthand, using indices (raised figures) but no multiplication signs:
(a) $p \times p$ (b) $3 \times r \times r$ (c) $4 \times a \times b$ (d) $7 \times a \times a \times b$ (e) $6 \times c \times c \times c$
(f) $c \times c \times d$ (g) $c \times d \times d$ (h) $2 \times c \times c \times d$ (i) $4 \times s \times s + 3 \times s$
(j) $k \times k \times k + k \times k$.

2 Write in full, as in the example in question 1:
  (a) x^3 (b) $2a^2$ (c) $3f^3$ (d) $3xy$ (e) $3x^2y$ (f) $3xy^2$ (g) $3x^2y^2$
  (h) $2d^2 + 5d$.

3 If $s = 1$, $t = 2$, $u = 3$ and $v = 4$, find the value of:
  (a) s^2t (b) t^2u (c) u^2v (d) st^2 (e) sv^2 (f) tu^2.

*4 If $p = 2$, $q = 3$ and $r = 5$, find the value of:
  (a) p^2 (b) p^2q (c) q^2r (d) pr^2 (e) qr^2 (f) p^2r.

5 The order in which we multiply numbers together does not matter, so $3 \times a \times 2 \times a \times a$ can be written as $3 \times 2 \times a \times a \times a$ which equals $6a^3$.

Similarly, $2 \times a \times b \times a \times 4 \times a \times b = 8a^3b^2$.

Note that the numbers are written first and the letters are usually written in alphabetical order.

Simplify:
  (a) $4 \times b \times 2$ (b) $3 \times a \times b \times a$ (c) $2 \times b \times a \times a \times a$
  (d) $7 \times a \times 8 \times b \times a \times b$ (e) $7 \times 9 \times a \times 2 \times a$ (f) $9 \times m \times m \times n \times m \times n$
  (g) $a \times b \times a \times c \times a \times b$ (h) $a \times b \times f \times 8 \times a \times 9 \times b \times c$.

6 **Example**   If 4 pencils cost x pence each then their total cost is $4x$ pence.

Write an expression, like $4x$ pence, for:

(a) the cost of 8 pencils at m pence each

(b) the cost of 6 cars at £q each

(c) the cost of 4 buns at m pence each and 5 cakes at x pence each

(d) the distance travelled in 2 hours at x km/h

(e) the distance travelled in 5 hours at x km/h

(f) the area of a rectangle if the length is l cm and the width is w cm

(g) the tax paid on £100 if one has to pay x pence for every £1 one earns

(h) the tax paid on £500 at x pence on every £1.

---

7 Write computer programs to check your answers to question 3.

8 Check your answers to question 6 by replacing the letters with the following numbers:
  $l = 15$; $m = 25$; $q = 5000$; $w = 5$; $x = 40$.

---

3   Integers: negative integers

A   Negative integers

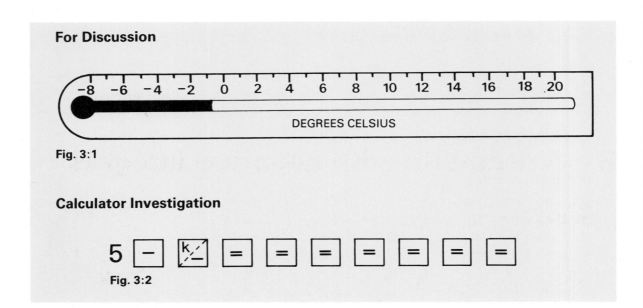

For Discussion

Fig. 3:1

Calculator Investigation

Fig. 3:2

1   Example   8°C > −3°C says '8°C is more than −3°C'.

Say which of the following is the higher temperature, writing your answers with a >
sign (not a < sign).
(a) 7°C; 10°C   (b) 6°C; −1°C   (c) −3°C; 10°C   (d) −2°C; 0°C
(e) −5°C; 5°C   (f) −4°C; −6°C

2   Examples   3 > −3 says '3 is more than −3'.
              −9 < −8 says '−9 is less than −8'.

Copy the following numbers, writing the correct sign, < or >, between them to make
a true statement.
(a) 6   4   (b) 3   7   (c) 1   0   (d) 0   2   (e) −3   0   (f) 2   −1
(g) −4   6   (h) −5   −8   (i) −9   −1   (j) −6   −4

3   Copy and continue for another five numbers the sequence:
(a) 6, 4, 2, 0   (b) 9, 6, 3   (c) 12, 11, 9, 6, 2   (d) 13, 11, 10, 8, 7, 5, 4.

4   **Example**   The numbers -9.5, $-9\frac{1}{4}$ and -9.1 all come between -10 and -9 on the number line.

Write any one number that is between:
(a) 10 and 9   (b) 8 and 7.5   (c) 6.4 and 6.3   (d) -4 and -3
(e) -8 and -7 (f) -1 and 0   (g) 0 and 1   (h) -1 and -2.3
(i) -1.5 and -1.7 (j) -7.1 and -7.2 (k) -8.4 and -8.5
(l) -3.1 and -3 (m) -4 and -4.05

5   Using your calculator, investigate arithmetic with negative integers. Write about your investigation.

B   Arithmetic with negative integers

For Discussion

−1   and   **−2**   makes   **−3**

Fig. 3:3

Calculator Investigation

What happens to the display when you press the $+/-$ key?

Try these sequences of key presses:

5 [+/−] [+]   3 [+/−] [=]   shows the answer to   **−5 + −3**

5 [+] 3 [+/−] [=]   shows the answer to   **5 + −3**

5 [+/−] [+] 3 [=]   shows the answer to   **−5 + 3**

Examples -8 and $-3 = -11$ $-8 - 3 = -11$
               8 and $-3 = 5$ $8 - 3 = 5$
               3 and $-8 = -5$ $3 - 8 = -5$

3

1 Add together:
(a) −3 and −1   (b) −6 and −4   (c) −4 and −8   (d) −5 and −2.

2 Add together:
(a) 3 and −1   (b) 6 and −4   (c) 8 and −4   (d) 5 and −2   (e) 9 and −3
(f) 16 and −12   (g) 20 and −10   (h) 3 and −3.

3 Add together:
(a) 4 and −5   (b) 7 and −8   (c) 3 and −5   (d) 2 and −7   (e) 4 and −6
(f) 1 and −6   (g) 3 and −9   (h) 0 and −8.

4 The 'and' can be omitted, so that −3 and −1 becomes just −3−1.

You may still find it helpful to *think* of this as '−3 and −1'.

Write the answers to the following:
(a) −7−4   (b) 6−6   (c) −7−9   (d) 8−11   (e) 4−9   (f) −3−8
(g) 2−11   (h) 4−6   (i) 14−15   (j) 23−26.

*5 (a) −3−4   (b) −8−2   (c) −5−2   (d) −4−1   (e) −8−9

*6 (a) 7−2   (b) 7−4   (c) 7−6   (d) 7−7   (e) 7−8   (f) 7−9
(g) 7−12   (h) 6−7   (i) 6−9   (j) 6−10

7 (a) 16−18   (b) 16−20   (c) 12−18   (d) 19−25   (e) 23−30
(f) 22−44

8 (a) −8+3   (b) −6+2   (c) −3+1   (d) −8+4   (e) −1+3
(f) −2+9   (g) −7+11   (h) −3+19   (i) −19+3   (j) −4+11

9 (a) −3−8   (b) 14−15   (c) 6−9   (d) 9−9   (e) 14−29

10 Look carefully at this pattern:

$$4 − 3 = 1$$
$$4 − 2 = 2$$
$$4 − 1 = 3$$
$$4 − 0 = 4$$

(a) What should come next after 3, 2, 1, 0?

(b) What should come next after 1, 2, 3, 4?

(c) Copy the pattern and write the next line.

14

11 Your answer to question 10(c) should have been $4 - -1 = 5$. Correct your answer if necessary, then write the next three lines of the pattern.

12 If $4 - -1 = 5$ then it must be true that $- -$ gives the same result as $+$, for $4 + 1 = 5$.

Similarly $4 - -2 = 6$ shows that $- -2$ gives the same result as $+2$.
Again, $4 - -3 \rightarrow 4 + 3 = 7$
And $4 - -4 \rightarrow 4 + 4 = 8$

Learn the rule: **Minus Minus makes Plus**

Work out:
(a) $6 - -5$ (b) $4 - -2$ (c) $3 - -5$ (d) $4 - -9$ (e) $12 - -8$
(f) $-2 - -4$ (g) $-3 - -1$ (h) $-7 - -6$.

13 If $a = 4$ and $b = -1$, what is the value of:
(a) $a + b$ (b) $b - a$ (c) $a - b$ (d) $2a + b$ (e) $2a - b$ (f) $3a - b$?

14 Copy and complete this table:

x	6	-3	-2	-9	-4	3	-9	1	-4	-6	-1.5	1.5
y	-2	4	-8	3	-9	-4	1	-9	-8	7	3	-3
$x + y$	4											
$x - y$	8											
$y - x$	-8											

---

15 Example   Find $-8 + 3 - 4 + 5 + 4$.

$$-8 \xrightarrow{+3} -5 \xrightarrow{-4} -9 \xrightarrow{+5} -4 \xrightarrow{+4} 0.$$

Find:
(a) $-7 - 2 + 4 - 3 + 4$ (b) $2 - 9 + 7 - 3 - 8 + 1$
(c) $4 + 3 - 2 + 1 - 7 - 8 - 1 + 6$.

16 Check your answers to question 15 with a calculator, then make up some similar examples. Work out the answers and check them with your calculator.

17 Using each of the figures 1 to 9 once only, write correct addition sums. You must use all nine figures. You could write correct ones on a wall poster. How many can you find? Write and tell us if you find more than 104!

Example $129 + 735 = 864$

4 Sets: two-sets notation

A Subsets

You should know the meaning of these phrases and symbols:
'list a set'; 'describe a set'; {. . .}; ∈; n( ); Ø.
You will find them explained in the Summaries of Book 1, on page 228.

A subset of a set is made up of some of the elements of the set.

Example If set $D = \{5, 7, 8\}$ then the subsets of set D are:
$\{5\}$; $\{7\}$; $\{8\}$; $\{5, 7\}$; $\{5, 8\}$; $\{7, 8\}$; $\{5, 7, 8\}$; $\{ \ \}$.

Note the last two, the set itself and the null set.

1 List the elements of sets A, B and C if:
$A = \{\text{traffic-light colours}\}$; $B = \{\text{months beginning with an A}\}$;
$C = \{\text{months beginning with a P}\}$.

2 In question 1, what is: (a) n(A)   (b) n(B)   (c) n(C)?

3 Describe: (a) $\{a, e, i, o, u\}$ (b) $\{\text{spring, summer, autumn, winter}\}$.

4 The elements of set S are the names of the shapes in Figure 4:1.

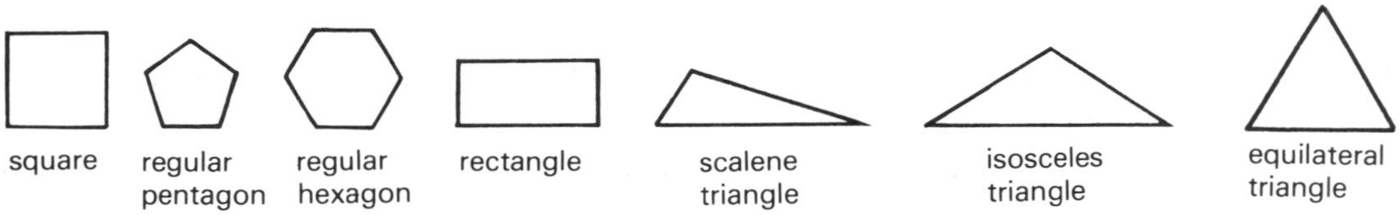

square   regular   regular   rectangle   scalene   isosceles   equilateral
          pentagon   hexagon   triangle   triangle   triangle

Fig. 4:1

(a) List the following subsets of S, noting that n(F) = 2, n(E) = 4 and n(D) = 1.
   (i) $F = \{\text{shapes with four sides}\}$
   (ii) $E = \{\text{shapes with all sides equal}\}$
   (iii) $D = \{\text{shapes with no equal sides}\}$

(b) Is a square an element of E?

(c) Isosceles triangle ∉ D. Why?

(d) What shape is x if $x \in F$ and $x \in E$?

5 (a) $N = \{1, 2\}$. List the four subsets of N.

(b) $P = \{1, 2, 3\}$. List the eight subsets of P.

16

*6 List the subsets of:
(a) {a, b}   (b) {a, b, c}.

7 If $B = \{1, 3, 5, 7, 8, 9, 12, 16\}$, list the following subsets of B.
(a) {prime numbers}   (b) {odd numbers}   (c) {even numbers}
(d) {square numbers}   (e) {multiples of 3}.

Note: Look up the words in the Glossary on pages 218 to 222 if you have forgotten what they mean.

8 List the following subsets of set S in question 4:

(a) $P = $ {shapes with opposite sides parallel}

(b) $A = $ {shapes with all angles equal}

(c) $T = $ {shapes with an angle sum of 180°}

(d) $Q = $ {shapes with an angle sum of 360°}.

---

9 List the subsets of:
(a) {a, b}   (b) {a, b, c}   (c) {a, b, c, d}.

10 Investigate, for each part of question 9, how many subsets have 4 elements, 3 elements, 2 elements, 1 element, and 0 elements. Find a connection between your answers and Pascal's triangle.

11 Investigate the number of subsets possible for a set with x elements, where x is any number.

B   Subset notation

The Venn diagram in Figure 4:2 shows that S is a subset of V.

$\supset$ and $\subset$ are the signs used to show that one set is a subset of another.

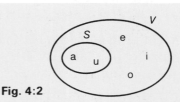

Fig. 4:2

$V \supset S$ means 'V contains S'; $S \subset V$ means 'S is a subset of V'.

{a, u} $\subset$ {a, e, i, o, u} means '{a, u} is a subset of {a, e, i, o, u}'

{a, t} $\not\subset$ {a, e, i, o, u} means '{a, t} is *not* a subset of {a, e, i, o, u}'

4

1 $B = \{3, 4, 5, 6, 7, 8, 9\}$.

   (a) List the following subsets of set B.
     O = {odd numbers}
     E = {even numbers}
     P = {prime numbers}
     S = {square numbers}
     M = {multiples of 4}
     F = {factors of 36}

   (b) Copy the following pairs of sets, writing $\subset$ or $\not\subset$ (not $\supset$ or $\not\supset$) between them to make true statements. For example, $P \subset B$; $S \not\subset E$.
     O P; E F; M E; S O; F S; E M.

   (c) Copy the pairs of sets in (b) again, this time writing $\supset$ or $\not\supset$ (not $\subset$ or $\not\subset$) between them to make true statements.

2 For Figure 4:3

   (a) List sets A and B.

   (b) Is $B \subset A$?

   (c) Does $A \supset B$?

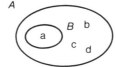

Fig. 4:3

3 For Figure 4:4

   (a) Describe clearly sets C and G.

   (b) Is $G \subset C$?

   (c) Does $G \supset C$?

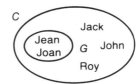

Fig. 4:4

4 Draw a Venn diagram to illustrate the sets:

   (a) {Mary, Anne, Mike, Fred} and {Anne, Mike}

   (b) {car, bicycle, yacht, bus, glider} and {yacht, glider}

   (c) A = {foods} and F = {fruit}, using the elements: biscuits, orange, pear and chips.

5 Using the sets in question 1, draw diagrams to show:
   (a) $O \subset B$ (b) $E \subset B$ (c) $B \supset P$ (d) $B \supset S$.

---

6 Copy Figure 4:5, then write in the elements of sets B, O and P from question 1. Find and illustrate other sets in question 1 which form this sort of diagram.

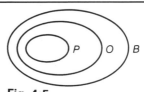

Fig. 4:5

C Disjoint and intersecting sets

Figure 4:6 shows two **disjoint** sets; they have no common elements.

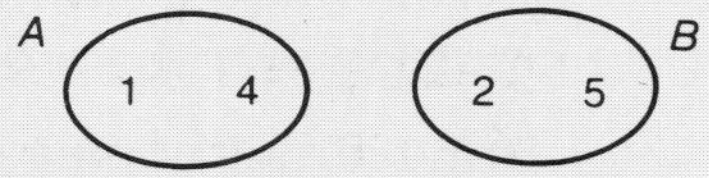

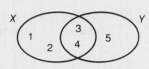

Fig. 4:6

Figure 4:7 shows two **intersecting** sets; they have the elements 3 and 4 in common.
$X = \{1, 2, 3, 4\}$ and $Y = \{3, 4, 5\}$.

The intersection of set X with set Y is written $X \cap Y$.

Fig. 4:7

Examples In Figures 4:6 and 4:7, $A \cap B = \emptyset$ and $X \cap Y = \{3, 4\}$.

1 For Figure 4:8 list the following sets, writing the answers in full, like $E = \{4, 7\}$ and $E \cap Z = \{5, 7, 9\}$. Write $\emptyset$ if there are no elements.
(a) A (b) B (c) $A \cap B$ (d) $P \cap Q$ (e) R (f) T (g) $R \cap T$ (h) $V \cap W$

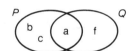

Fig. 4:8

2 $C = \{1, 2, 3\}$; $D = \{1, 2\}$; $E = \{3, 4\}$; $F = \{5, 6, 7\}$

(a) Which set is a subset of C?   (b) Which set intersects with E?

(c) Which set is disjoint with C?

(d) Use the correct type of Venn diagram (see Figure 4:8) to illustrate sets:
(i) C and D (ii) C and E (iii) C and F.

(e) List:
(i) $C \cap D$ (ii) $C \cap E$ (iii) $C \cap F$.

*3 For Figure 4:9, list set:
(a) A (b) B (c) $A \cap B$ (d) $C \cap D$ (e) E (f) F (g) $E \cap F$ (h) $G \cap H$.

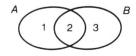 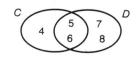 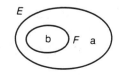 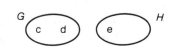

Fig. 4:9

4

*4

  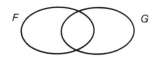

Fig. 4:10

In Figure 4:10, F = {5, 8, 9}; G = {5, 6}; H = {3, 9}; I = {5, 6, 7, 8, 9}.

(a) Draw larger copies of the Venn diagrams and write in the elements.

(b) Draw the correct type of Venn diagram and write in the elements for sets:
(i) F and H   (ii) G and I   (iii) H and I.

5   A = {factors of 24}; B = {factors of 48};
C = {factors of 20}; D = {factors of 100}.

(a) Lists sets A, B, C and D.

(b) Check that n(A) = 8, n(B) = 10, n(C) = 6 and n(D) = 9, then draw Venn diagrams to illustrate the pair of sets:
(i) A and C   (ii) A and B   (iii) A and D   (iv) C and D.

---

6   Lewis Carroll, the author of *Alice's Adventures in Wonderland*, developed his own way of classifying information which he called Carroll diagrams.

Example

30	45	Ripe
50	10	Not ripe
Large	Not large	

This diagram represents the contents of a box of apples. Check that the following information is true.

(a) There are 75 ripe apples and 60 apples that are not ripe.
(b) There are 80 large apples and 55 which are not large.
(c) There are 135 apples.
(d) There are 50 large apples which are not ripe and 30 which are ripe.
(e) There are 10 apples which are not large and not ripe.

7   This Carroll diagram represents the pupils in class 2B.
How many are (a) boys (b) girls (c) tall
(d) not tall (e) boys who are not tall
(f) tall girls (g) girls who are not tall?
(h) How many pupils are there in class 2B?

7	8	Boys
10	3	Girls
Tall	Not tall	

8   Draw a Carroll diagram to represent: *Girl, Boy, Goes home for lunch, Does not go home for lunch* for your class.

D Union

The **union** of two sets is the set made by uniting (putting together) their elements.

Elements common to both sets only count once.

The union of set *X* with set *Y* is written *X* ∪ *Y*.

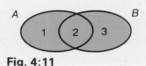

Example   In Figure 4:11, *A* = {1, 2} and *B* = {2, 3}, so *A* ∪ *B* = {1, 2, 3}.

Fig. 4:11

1   Writing the answer in full, like *X* = {4, 8, 9}, list from Figure 4:12 the set:
(a) *A*   (b) *B*   (c) *A* ∩ *B*   (d) *A* ∪ *B*   (e) *C* ∩ *D*   (f) *C* ∪ *D*
(g) *E*   (h) *F*   (i) *E* ∩ *F*   (j) *E* ∪ *F*.

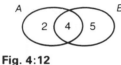   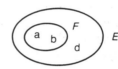

Fig. 4:12

2   List the union of:
(a) {a, b, c} and {a, c}   (b) {1, 2} and {2, 3, 4}
(c) {red, white} and {red, white, green}   (d) {4, 5} and {6, 7}.

*3   List the union of: (a) {1, 4} and {4, 5, 6}   (b) {a, b, c} and {b, c, d, e}.

4   Remember that 1 is not a rectangular number nor a prime number, but it is a triangular number.

(a) List the sets:
    O = {odd numbers from 1 to 9};   *R* = {the first four rectangular numbers}
    P = {prime numbers from 2 to 11};   *N* = {factors of 9}
    T = {the first four triangular numbers}.

(b) Choose from the three types of Venn diagram in Figure 4:12 to illustrate the following pairs of sets, writing in the elements and labelling each set.
    N and *P*; *N* and *O*; *N* and *R*; *P* and *R*; *T* and *O*.

(c) List the sets:
    N ∩ *O*; *P* ∩ *R*; *T* ∪ *P*; *N* ∪ *T*; *R* ∩ *T*; *O* ∪ *R*.

5 If $A \subset B$ what is: (a) $A \cup B$ (b) $A \cap B$?

6 $T = \{\text{teachers}\}$; $S = \{\text{people over six-feet tall}\}$;
$R = \{\text{right-handed people}\}$; $C = \{\text{car owners}\}$.

Describe:
(a) $T \cap S$ (b) $T \cup S$ (c) $T \cap R$ (d) $T \cup R$ (e) $T \cap C$ (f) $T \cup C$.

How many sets does your teacher come into?

Write four different sets to which you belong, then say to which sets, including their unions and intersections, some other people known to you belong.

E   Venn diagrams showing n( )

Figure 4:13 shows the *number* of members in sets D and C, not what the elements are. Set D has 16 members. Set C has 25 members.

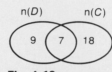

Fig. 4:13

1 In Figure 4:13
$D = \{\text{pupils in form 2X who own a dog}\}$
$C = \{\text{pupils in form 2X who own a cat}\}$.

(a) How many pupils own:
  (i) a dog   (ii) a cat   (iii) both   (iv) a dog but not a cat
  (v) a cat but not a dog?

(b) How many is:
  (i) n(C)   (ii) n(D)   (iii) n($C \cap D$)   (iv) n($C \cup D$)?

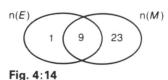

***2** In Figure 4:14
$E = \{\text{pupils in form 2M who like English}\}$
$M = \{\text{pupils in form 2M who like Mathematics}\}$.

Fig. 4:14

(a) How many pupils like:
  (i) English   (ii) Mathematics   (iii) both
  (iv) English but not Mathematics   (v) Mathematics but not English?

(b) How many is:
  (i) n(E)   (ii) n(M)   (iii) n($M \cap E$)   (iv) n($E \cup M$)?

3 Draw a Venn diagram to show:

(a) n(A) = 7, n(B) = 5, n(A ∩ B) = 3

(b) n(C) = 5, n(D) = 8, n(C ∩ D) = 4

(c) n(E) = 9, n(F) = 13, n(E ∩ F) = 7.

4 Copy Figure 4:15 and complete it so that n(B) = 8.

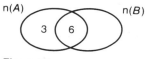

Fig. 4:15

Check that n(A) + n(B) = 17 and that n(A ∪ B) = 11.

The difference between these gives the number in A ∩ B, that is 17 − 11 = 6.

Draw a Venn diagram to show:

(a) n(G) = 11, n(H) = 3, n(G ∪ H) = 12

(b) n(I) = 15, n(J) = 8, n(I ∪ J) = 20

(c) n(K) = 20, n(L) = 16, n(K ∪ L) = 28

(d) n(M) = 15, n(N) = 13, n(M ∪ N) = 27.

---

5 30 pupils all play hockey or tennis or both. 18 play hockey and 20 play tennis.

(a) Using sets H and T draw a Venn diagram to illustrate this.

(b) How many play both sports?

6 All 29 pupils in a room are either girls or prefects or both. There are 27 girls and 6 prefects. How many girl prefects are there in the room?

7 Some of the following sets are intersecting, some are subsets, and some are disjoint. Decide which is which, then draw a Venn diagram to illustrate the number of elements in the sets.

(a) n(A) = 6, n(B) = 5, n(A ∪ B) = 10

(b) n(C) = 7, n(D) = 4, n(C ∪ D) = 7

(c) n(E) = 15, n(F) = 14, n(E ∩ F) = 7

(d) n(G) = 12, n(H) = 8, n(G ∩ H) = 0

(e) n(I) = 16, n(J) = 11, n(I ∪ J) = 16

(f) n(K) = 13, n(L) = 12, n(K ∪ L) = 25

(g) n(M) = 6, n(N) = 6, n(M ∪ N) = 7

5 Decimal fractions: division

A Review of decimal fractions

You should not need to use a calculator for any question in this exercise.

1 Copy Figure 5:1 and complete the column headings.

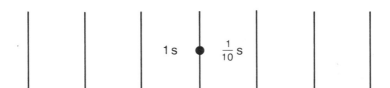

1 s • $\frac{1}{10}$ s

Fig. 5:1

2 In the number 623.81 the 2 is worth 20 and the 1 is worth $\frac{1}{100}$.

What is the value of:
(a) the 6 (b) the 3 (c) the 8?

3 Add ten to:
(a) 6 (b) 6.8 (c) 93 (d) 0.5

4 Add one tenth to:
(a) 6.7 (b) 8 (c) 0.5 (d) 4.26

5 Write in order of size, largest first:
(a) 1.4; 1.2; 2.1; 0.4; 1.3 (b) 2.65; 2.6; 2.5; 2.55; 2.56

6 (a) Add 17.3 to 8.5 (b) Take 8.5 from 17.3 (c) 16 + 3.9 (d) 18 − 5.3

7 (a) Add £18, £3.06, £4.20 and £7 (b) Add 18, 3.06, 4.2 and 7

8 (a)   4.306   (b)   6.51
      − 1.72   − 1.934

9 (a) 1.9×6 (b) 2.3×4.2 (c) 8.01×6.7

10 (a) 2.3×10 (b) 2.32×10 (c) 8.6×100 (d) 8.65×100

*11 State the value of each figure in 316.95

*12 Add one tenth to each number in question 3.

*13 (a) Add 16.1 to 5.38   (b) Subtract 3.46 from 7.09   (c) Subtract 18.6 from 125
(d) Subtract 4.02 from 74.9

*14 Multiply: (a) 1.4 by 7   (b) 6.3 by 2.4   (c) 5.01 by 3.6

*15 Multiply by ten:
(a) 6   (b) 6.8   (c) 6.84   (d) 7.75   (e) 15.02

*16 Multiply 100 by:
(a) 7   (b) 75   (c) 7.5   (d) 6.75   (e) 0.75

17 Take one tenth away from:
(a) 7.6   (b) 6.1   (c) 2.93   (d) 2.13   (e) 2.0   (f) 3   (g) 8.05   (h) 6.02

18 Take one hundredth away from:
(a) 1.62   (b) 0.75   (c) 6.30   (d) 4.2   (e) 7.00   (f) 9

19 Write one tenth of each of the numbers in question 18.

20 Write one hundredth of each of the numbers in question 18.

21 Write as a decimal fraction:
(a) 6 tenths   (b) 7 hundredths   (c) 67 hundredths   (d) 80 hundredths
(e) 1 thousandth.

22 How many metres is:
(a) 1 km   (b) 0.1 km   (c) 0.01 km   (d) 0.001 km   (e) 0.2 km
(f) 0.26 km   (g) 0.267 km?

23 Draw accurately a square of side 4.7 cm. Calculate its area in cm^2. How many whole
centimetre squares can you draw in your square?

24 (a) How many millimetres is each side of the square that you drew in question 23?
(b) What is the area of your square in mm²?

25 How many mm² is:
(a) 6.12 cm²   (b) 5 cm²   (c) 4.1 cm²?

26 Write as a decimal of a metre:
(a) 1 cm   (b) 4 cm   (c) 4.7 cm.

27 How many square metres is the area of the square in question 23?

---

28 8 + 3 = 11 is the sum for the story: *'Jane has 8 text-books and 3 exercise books. She has 11 books altogether.'*

Make up a story for the sum 8.4 + 2.5 = 10.9

29 Write any four-digit number (like 3167). Rewrite it underneath with the digits in a different order (like 1637). Subtract. Will your answer divide by 9? Try again with a new number. When can you *not* subtract? Does your answer always divide by 9? Why?

30
```
0  1  2  3  4  ...
0  1  2  3  ...
```

(a) Continue the above sequences until the bottom one reaches 9. Add the pairs of numbers. Describe the pattern of the answer.

(b) What happens if you move the bottom row another place to the right?

(c) Try putting other rows from 0 to 9 in various positions underneath the top row.

B   Review of integer division

For Discussion

How many ways can you find to write '12 divided by 3' in mathematical notation?

How many different words and phrases that mean the same as divide can you find?

1 Divide the following numbers by 7.
(a) 1764   (b) 3213   (c) 6615   (d) 12789.

2

n	1	2	3	4	5	6	7	8	9
$17n$	17	34	51	68	85	102	119	136	153

Using the above table to help you, divide the following numbers by 17.
(a) 918   (b) 3655   (c) 15096.

*3 Divide the numbers in question 1 by nine.

*4 Divide the following numbers by 4.
(a) 3.16   (b) 131.00   (c) 407.00

*5 Divide the following numbers by 5, putting 0s as necessary to give a decimal fraction answer.
(a) 3   (b) 7   (c) 9   (d) 11   (e) 21   (f) 47

*6 Divide the following numbers by 17.
(a) 612   (b) 391   (c) 595   (d) 3468

7 Divide the numbers in question 5 by 8.

8 By dividing the top number by the bottom number, change to a decimal fraction:
(a) $\frac{1}{8}$ (b) $\frac{5}{8}$ (c) $\frac{1}{16}$ (d) $\frac{3}{16}$

9 When a number is divided by 10 each figure moves one column 'down' (to the right).

When a number is divided by 100 each figure moves two columns 'down'.

Examples $315 \div 10 = 31.5$; $45.03 \div 10 = 4.503$; $3.61 \div 100 = 0.0361$

Copy and complete this table:

n	7	14	3.1	4.9	0.6	0.8	1.83	0.67
$n \times 10$								
$n \times 100$								
$n \div 10$								
$n \div 100$								

10 State the value of the letter if:
   (a) $16 \div a = 1.6$ (b) $23 \times b = 230$ (c) $4.9 \div c = 0.49$ (d) $3.2 \div d = 0.032$
   (e) $0.35 \div e = 0.035$ (f) $4 \div f = 0.004$ (g) $1.52 \times g = 152$
   (h) $4.06 \times h = 4060$ (i) $i \times 10 = 0.1$ (j) $j \times 100 = 0.4$ (k) $k \div 10 = 0.016$

11 Divide each of the following by 3, 6, 7 and 9, stopping as soon as you notice the figures after the decimal point repeating themselves.
   (a) 10   (b) 12   (c) 1.6

12 A number like 3.333 . . . is called a **recurring decimal**. We write it as $3.\dot{3}$, the dot above the 3 showing that it repeats endlessly.

Similarly, 0.016 161 6 . . . would be written $0.0\dot{1}\dot{6}$
and 1.285 714 285 714 . . . as $1.\dot{2}857 1\dot{4}$

Write your answers to question 11 with recurrence dots.

13 Investigate the recurrence of $\frac{1}{7}$, $\frac{2}{7}$, etc. up to $\frac{6}{7}$.

Include in the report of your findings an explanation of the absence of the figures 0, 3, 6 and 9 in the recurrence pattern and why the division must recur after six figures.

14 Investigate the recurrence of divisions by:
   (a) 3   (b) 11   (c) 37   (d) 101   (e) 41 and 271   (f) 7 and 13.

15 Find other numbers that divide to give recurrence. You will find the calculator display too short for some of them. Can you overcome this problem?

C   Division of decimals by decimals

You may be allowed to use a calculator for at least some of this exercise.

When not using a calculator you have to change both numbers in the division so that you are dividing by a whole number.

Examples $3.8 \div 0.2 \to \frac{3.8}{0.2} \to \frac{3.8 \times 10}{0.2 \times 10} \to \frac{38}{2} = 19$

$1.236 \div 0.03 \to \frac{1.236 \times 100}{0.03 \times 100} \to \frac{123.6}{3} = 41.2$

1 (a) $2.4 \div 0.2$ (b) $7.6 \div 0.2$ (c) $8.24 \div 0.2$ (d) $0.824 \div 0.2$

2 (a) $12.3 \div 0.3$ (b) $1.23 \div 0.3$ (c) $1.23 \div 0.03$ (d) $12.3 \div 0.003$

*3 (a) $6.4 \div 0.2$ (b) $48 \div 0.2$ (c) $36.8 \div 0.4$ (d) $5.6 \div 0.02$

4 Do the work in brackets first:
(a) $(4.4 + 3.2) \div 0.4$ (b) $(7 - 3.1) \div 0.3$ (c) $(8 - 2.96) \div 0.06$ (d) $(4 \div 4) \div 5$
(e) $4 \div (4 \div 5)$ (f) $(6 \times 3) \div 4$ (g) $6 \times (3 \div 4)$

5 Which of the following are *untrue*?

(a) $(6 + 3) + 0.4 = 6 + (3 + 0.4)$ (b) $(6 + 3) - 0.4 = 6 + (3 - 0.4)$

(c) $(6 - 3) + 0.4 = 6 - (3 + 0.4)$ (d) $(6 - 3) - 0.4 = 6 - (3 - 0.4)$

(e) $(6 \times 3) \div 0.4 = 6 \times (3 \div 0.4)$ (f) $(6 \div 3) \times 0.4 = 6 \div (3 \times 0.4)$

(g) $(6 \times 3) \times 0.4 = 6 \times (3 \times 0.4)$ (h) $(6 \div 3) \div 0.4 = 6 \div (3 \div 0.4)$

6 (a) A sheet of stamps is 35.2 cm long and 21.6 cm wide. How many stamps in the sheet if each stamp is 2.2 cm by 1.8 cm?

(b) There are 11 perforations (holes) along the length of one stamp. How many perforations should there be along the width of one stamp?

(c) What is the area of one stamp in:
(i) cm^2 (ii) mm^2?

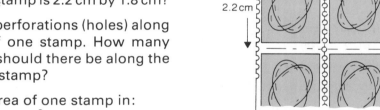

Fig. 5:2

7 Kaprekar's constant: a calculator investigation

(a)
Write down a number with four different digits.

Arrange the digits in order, largest first.

Arrange the digits in order, smallest first.

Subtract the numbers formed by the last two steps.

Write down the answer.

(b) Investigate the result if you start with longer or shorter numbers.

Using Your Calculator

The Pony Express

WANTED

PONY EXPRESS RIDER

March 1860
Young, skinny, wiry
fellows wanted, not over
18. Must be expert riders,
willing to risk death daily.

Orphans preferred.

This advertisement was posted by two businessmen who set out to improve the postal service across the U.S.A. between Washington and San Francisco, which then took three weeks by the safe, but long, southern route.

The Pony Express was to take the direct route, 1900 miles of dangerous Indian territories, to Sacramento.

A hundred and fifty relay stations, spaced 5 to 25 miles apart, were supported by 400 horses and 80 riders, making two runs each way, each run taking 10 days.

'Pony Bob' Haslam once covered 190 miles in a record 18 hours when a relief rider refused to ride. Then, after only a couple of hours rest, he turned and rode all the way back.

From April 3, 1860 to October 24, 1861 the riders braved the weather and the Indians; then the completion of the telegraph line made them obsolete.

Use the above information and your calculator to answer the following questions.

1 Calculate the average distance between the relay stations.

2 Calculate the average distance covered by each horse, assuming all are used.

3 Calculate the average distance covered per day.

4 Calculate the average speed of the Pony Express in miles per hour.

5 What was Pony Bob's average speed on his record-breaking run?

6 For how many days did the Pony Express exist?

6 Matrices: addition and subtraction

A Using a matrix

One Monday morning Jasbir, Marion and Mary check their coins.

The table, or **matrix**, shows the result.

Coin:	£1	50p	20p	10p	5p	2p	1p
Jasbir	1	2	0	0	0	2	1
Marion	0	1	3	0	2	3	5
Mary	1	0	1	4	4	1	2

From the matrix we can see that Jasbir has one £1 coin, two 50p's, two 2p's and one 1p; he has £2.05 altogether.

1 (a) Write a sentence, like the one above, about Marion.
   (b) How much have the three children altogether?
   (c) How many coins does each have?

2 The following Monday the headings for the matrix are the same, so they just write the numbers:

   (a) How many 50p's altogether this week?
   (b) How many 2p's altogether this week?
   (c) How many 5p's does Marion have?
   (d) How many 10p's does Mary have?
   (e) How much have the three children altogether this week?

$$\begin{pmatrix} 0 & 1 & 2 & 1 & 2 & 3 & 0 \\ 1 & 2 & 1 & 0 & 0 & 1 & 1 \\ 2 & 1 & 2 & 2 & 3 & 5 & 2 \end{pmatrix}$$

3 Marion records the total numbers of coins the three children had for both weeks. Copy and complete her table.

$$\begin{pmatrix} 1 & 3 & 2 & 1 & 2 & 5 & 1 \\ 1 & & & & & & \\ 3 & & & & & & \end{pmatrix}$$

4 After another week Marion's table looks like this:

$$\begin{pmatrix} 3 & 5 & 4 & 2 & 2 & 5 & 7 \\ 1 & 5 & 4 & 2 & 2 & 4 & 8 \\ 3 & 1 & 3 & 6 & 7 & 6 & 4 \end{pmatrix}$$

   (a) Which child had no coins in the third week?
   (b) Work out the table for how many coins each child had in the third week.

5 The number of people living in a house can be shown as a matrix.

Write matrices for some of your relations and neighbours.

	Males	Females
Adults (over 16)	1	2
Children	2	3

B Order of a matrix; addition; subtraction

$$U = \begin{pmatrix} 2 & 3 & 4 \\ 1 & 6 & 1 \end{pmatrix} \quad V = \begin{pmatrix} 4 & 2 & 5 \\ 1 & 8 & 7 \end{pmatrix} \quad X = \begin{pmatrix} 2 & 1 \\ 4 & 6 \end{pmatrix} \quad Y = (3 \ 5 \ 7) \quad Z = \begin{pmatrix} 3 \\ 4 \\ 8 \end{pmatrix}$$

The order of a matrix is stated as its number of rows by its number of columns.

For the above matrices:

U and V are rectangular matrices of order 2 by 3 (2 rows, 3 columns).

X is a square matrix of order 2 by 2.

Y is a row matrix of order 1 by 3.

Z is a column matrix of order 3 by 1.

Matrices of the same order can be added and subtracted, as we did for the coins matrices in the previous exercise.

Examples
$$U + V = \begin{pmatrix} 2 & 3 & 4 \\ 1 & 6 & 1 \end{pmatrix} + \begin{pmatrix} 4 & 2 & 5 \\ 1 & 8 & 7 \end{pmatrix} = \begin{pmatrix} 6 & 5 & 9 \\ 2 & 14 & 8 \end{pmatrix}$$

$$U - V = \begin{pmatrix} 2 & 3 & 4 \\ 1 & 6 & 1 \end{pmatrix} - \begin{pmatrix} 4 & 2 & 5 \\ 1 & 8 & 7 \end{pmatrix} = \begin{pmatrix} -2 & 1 & -1 \\ 0 & -2 & -6 \end{pmatrix}$$

The following program adds and subtracts any two matrices of the same order. It has been written to work on many different computers, but you may need to change PAUSE and CLS.
Lines 620 to 670 should adjust the spacing to produce a tidy matrix; you can use PRINT USING instead.

Subroutines
To save program lines, subroutines are used, the same subroutine being used more than once at different points in the program. On a BBC you can use PROC.
360 to 480 input the matrix and print it.
490 to 610 calculate and display the sum and difference of the two matrices.
620 to 680 adjust spacing to allow for +/− and one to three digits.

Matrices
The numbers in the matrices are recorded using a 'two-dimensional array', F. Both matrices are recorded in the same array. If both matrices are 2 rows, 3 columns, then the numbers are stored as follows:

$$\begin{pmatrix} F(1,1) & F(1,2) & F(1,3) \\ F(2,1) & F(2,2) & F(2,3) \end{pmatrix}; \quad \begin{pmatrix} F(3,1) & F(3,2) & F(3,3) \\ F(4,1) & F(4,2) & F(4,3) \end{pmatrix}$$

```
  5 REM "Matrix1"
 10 PRINT "Type order of matrices to be combined."
 20 PRINT "How  many  rows  (r)?  How  many  columns  (c)?  Type ∧ r ∧
    RETURN ∧ c ∧ RETURN."
    (∧ means leave a space)
 25 CLEAR    (Omit on Spectrum)
 30 INPUT R
 40 INPUT C
 50 DIM F(R∗2, C)
 60 LET A = 1
 70 LET B = R
 80 LET J = 0
 90 LET M$ = " ∧ first ∧"
100 CLS    (Clear screen)
110 GOSUB 360
120 LET A = R + 1
130 LET B = R∗2
140 LET M$ = " ∧ second ∧"
150 GOSUB 360
160 LET J = 1
170 PAUSE 100    (1 second pause)
180 CLS    (Clear screen)
190 PRINT " ∧∧ A = ∧";
200 LET A = 1
210 LET B = R
220 GOSUB 380
230 PRINT
240 PRINT " ∧∧ B = ∧";
250 LET A = R + 1
260 LET B = R∗2
270 GOSUB 380
280 PRINT
290 LET E = 0
300 GOSUB 490
310 PRINT
320 LET E = 1
330 GOSUB 490
340 PRINT
350 GOTO 10
360 PRINT "Type in";M$;"matrix,"
370 PRINT "row  by  row.  Press
    RETURN after each number."
380 FOR M = A TO B
390 PRINT "(";

400 FOR N = 1 TO C
410 IF J = 0 THEN INPUT F(M, N)
420 LET D = F(M, N)
425 IF J = 0 THEN GOTO 440
        (This line may not be needed)
430 GOSUB 620
440 NEXT N
450 PRINT ")"
460 IF J = 1 THEN PRINT " ∧∧∧∧∧";
470 NEXT M
480 RETURN
490 IF E = 0 THEN PRINT "A + B = ∧";
500 IF E = 1 THEN PRINT "A − B = ∧";
510 FOR M = 1 TO R
520 PRINT "(";
530 FOR N = 1 TO C
540 IF E = 0 THEN LET D = F(M,
    N) + F(M + R, N)
550 IF E = 1 THEN LET D = F(M,
    N) − F(M + R, N)
560 GOSUB 620
570 NEXT N
580 PRINT ")"
590 PRINT " ∧∧∧∧∧";
600 NEXT M
610 RETURN
620 LET L = LEN (STR$ (D))
630 IF L = 1 THEN PRINT " ∧∧∧";
640 IF L = 2 THEN PRINT " ∧∧";
650 IF L = 3 THEN PRINT " ∧";
660 PRINT ;D;
670 PRINT " ∧";
680 RETURN
```

Use the following matrices in questions 1 to 6.

$$A = \begin{pmatrix} 1 & 2 & 3 \\ 0 & 1 & 2 \\ 4 & 6 & 5 \end{pmatrix} \quad B = \begin{pmatrix} 2 \\ 4 \\ 6 \end{pmatrix} \quad C = \begin{pmatrix} 2 & 4 & 5 \\ 1 & 0 & 6 \end{pmatrix} \quad D = \begin{pmatrix} 4 & 1 \\ 0 & 5 \\ 7 & 8 \end{pmatrix} \quad E = \begin{pmatrix} 3 & 1 & 4 \\ 5 & 1 & 6 \end{pmatrix} \quad F = (5 \ 4 \ 1)$$

$$G = \begin{pmatrix} 4 & 6 \\ 0 & 0 \\ 1 & 4 \end{pmatrix} \quad H = \begin{pmatrix} 5 & 4 & 2 \\ 0 & 1 & 0 \\ 6 & 5 & 3 \end{pmatrix} \quad J = (2 \ 4 \ 6) \quad K = \begin{pmatrix} 5 \\ 2 \\ 7 \end{pmatrix} \quad L = \begin{pmatrix} 2 & 4 & 2 \\ 1 & 1 & 3 \\ 5 & 6 & 1 \end{pmatrix} \quad M = \begin{pmatrix} 2 & 5 & 1 \\ 1 & 3 & 4 \end{pmatrix}$$

1 Write the type and order of matrices A to H (not J to M).

Work out the answers in questions 2 and 3 if possible, or else write 'impossible'.

2 (a) $A + H$ (b) $A + C$ (c) $C + E$ (d) $A + F$ (e) $F + J$ (f) $D + G$

3 (a) $A - H$ (b) $C - E$ (c) $B - F$ (d) $F - J$ (e) $D - G$ (f) $B - K$

*4 Write the type and order of matrices J to M.

*5 State which of the following have no meaning. *Do not work out* the possible ones.
    (a) $C + M$ (b) $A + L$ (c) $M + J$ (d) $F + K$ (e) $M + E$ (f) $B + J$

*6 Work out, if possible: (a) $C - M$ (b) $A - L$ (c) $M - A$ (d) $H - L$.

7 $A = \begin{pmatrix} 2 & -2 \\ -1 & 0 \end{pmatrix} \quad\quad B = \begin{pmatrix} -4 & -2 \\ 1 & 3 \end{pmatrix} \quad\quad C = \begin{pmatrix} -6 & 4 \\ 2 & -3 \end{pmatrix} \quad\quad D = \begin{pmatrix} 5 & 2 \\ -3 & 4 \end{pmatrix}$

Find:
(a) $A + B$ (b) $C + D$ (c) $A - B$ (d) $B - C$ (e) $A - D$ (f) $B - D$.

8 $M = \begin{pmatrix} 1 & -3 \\ 2 & 2 \end{pmatrix} \quad\quad N = \begin{pmatrix} -2 & 0 \\ 2 & 1 \end{pmatrix} \quad\quad P = \begin{pmatrix} 6 & -3 \\ 0 & 1 \end{pmatrix}$

Find:
(a) $M + N$ (b) $M - N$ (c) $N - P$ (d) $P - M$ (e) $M + N + P$
(f) $M + N - P$ (g) $M - N - P$ (h) $M - P - N$ (i) $M + M$ (j) $M + M + M$.

9 $A = \begin{pmatrix} -2.4 & 4.7 \\ 3.6 & -5.3 \end{pmatrix}; \quad B = \begin{pmatrix} 1.8 & -4.6 \\ -3.7 & -2.8 \end{pmatrix}; \quad C = \begin{pmatrix} 4.2 & -1.4 \\ -9.6 & 3.7 \end{pmatrix}.$

Work out in your head:
(a) $2A$ (b) $3B$ (c) $4C$ (d) $A - C$ (e) $C - A$ (f) $A - B$
(g) $B - C$ (h) $C - B$.

7 Integers: + and − with negatives

A Combining + and −

For Discussion

$6 - 2 = 4$ (a) What should come after:
$6 - 1 = 5$ (i) the 2, 1, 0   (ii) the 4, 5, 6?
$6 - 0 = 6$ (b) How should the pattern continue?

Examples $6 - -1 \rightarrow 6 + 1 = 7$

$8 - -3 \rightarrow 8 + 3 = 11$

Using a Calculator

$6 - -1$ is keyed in as   6 $\boxed{-}$ 1 $\boxed{+/-}$ $\boxed{=}$

$3 - 8$ is keyed in as   3 $\boxed{-}$ 8 $\boxed{=}$

Watch the display carefully as you key these in.

1 Remember that $-5 - 9$ means 'start at -5 and go down 9', giving the answer -14.
Find:
(a) $-9 - 3$ (b) $-3 - 7$ (c) $-5 - 12$ (d) $-19 - 8$ (e) $-27 - 13$.

2 Remember that $5 - 9$ means 'start at 5 and go down 9', giving the answer -4.
Find:
(a) $4 - 6$ (b) $5 - 7$ (c) $8 - 12$ (d) $7 - 11$ (e) $2 - 6$.

3 Use a calculator to check your answers to questions 1 and 2. If you had any wrong, think again, and ask your teacher for help if necessary.

4 Line AB in Figure 7:1 shows that $2 - 3 = -1$. What does line CD show?

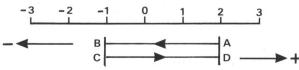

Fig. 7:1

5 Your last answer should have been $-1 + 3 = 2$.

Similarly, $-2 + 3 = 1$ (start at -2 and move up 3).

Find:
(a) $-2 + 4$ (b) $-3 + 6$ (c) $-3 + 5$ (d) $-3 + 4$ (e) $-3 + 3$
(f) $-3 + 2$ (g) $-1 + 1$.

6 Find:
(a) $6 - -2$ (b) $9 - -4$ (c) $3 - -9$ (d) $8 - -7$.

7 Find:
(a) $-8 + 10$ (b) $8 - 10$ (c) $-9 - 9$ (d) $9 - -9$ (e) $8 - -10$.

*8 Think of $-8 + 12$ as meaning 'start at -8, then go up 12'.

After you have gone up 8 you will be at 0, then you have 4 more to go, so $-8 + 12 = 4$.

Find:
(a) $-4 + 5$ (b) $-6 + 8$ (c) $-10 + 11$ (d) $-12 + 14$ (e) $-13 + 15$
(f) $-5 + 9$ (g) $-4 + 7$ (h) $-8 + 10$ (i) $-5 + 6$ (j) $-5 + 5$
(k) $-5 + 4$ (l) $-5 + 3$ (m) $-5 + 2$ (n) $-5 + 1$.

*9 Think of $6 - 9$ as meaning 'start at 6, then go down 9'.

After you have gone down 6 you will be at 0, then you have 3 more to go, so $6 - 9 = -3$.

Similarly, $-6 - 9$ is 'start at -6 then go down 9', so $-6 - 9 = -15$.

Find.
(a) $4 - 7$ (b) $3 - 7$ (c) $6 - 7$ (d) $8 - 8$ (e) $4 - 9$ (f) $2 - 13$
(g) $1 - 15$ (h) $-7 - 6$ (i) $-9 - 11$ (j) $-8 - 12$ (k) $-4 - 15$
(l) $-13 - 12$ (m) $-21 - 36$ (n) $-42 - 20$.

*10 Remember that $- -$ becomes $+$, so $7 - -8 \rightarrow 7 + 8 = 15$.

Find:
(a) $6 - -3$ (b) $7 - -7$ (c) $8 - -7$ (d) $7 - -9$ (e) $6 - -6$
(f) $9 - -9$ (g) $5 - -12$ (h) $13 - -15$.

*11 **Examples** $-4 + 6 = 2$ $4 - 6 = -2$ $4 - -6 = 10$

Find:
(a) $-7 + 1$ (b) $7 - -1$ (c) $-7 - 3$ (d) $7 - -3$ (e) $-7 + 3$
(f) $3 - 7$ (g) $1 - 7$ (h) $-1 - 7$.

12 Example $-5--4 \rightarrow -5+4 = -1$

Find:
(a) $-6--3$ (b) $-8--2$ (c) $-5--1$ (d) $-4--1$ (e) $-1+4$.

13 A useful rule for harder numbers, when one is $+$ and the other is $-$, is:
Sign of the bigger; difference between them.

Find: (a) $76-145$ (b) $31.16-14.28$ (c) $14.28-31.16$ (d) $16.9-29.3$

14 Find: (a) $7-3.8$ (b) $6-9.4$ (c) $3-4.68$ (d) $-46+319$.

15 Find: (a) $-8.71+16.29$ (b) $-3+6.5$ (c) $-1+0.47$ (d) $-5+0.98$

16 Copy and complete this table, which gives all the ways that x, y and z can be added and subtracted.

Take $x=9$, $y=-7$ and $z=4.8$

	ADD			SUBTRACT		
	x	y	z	x	y	z
x	18				16	
y				-16		
z						

17 Figure 7:2 is a nomogram. Scale C gives the answer to $A+B$.

Example To find $-3+2$.
Line up the -3 on the A line with the 2 on the B line, using a ruler.
The ruler crosses the C line at -1, so $-3+2 = -1$.

Use the nomogram to find:
(a) $3+2$ (b) $3+-2$ (c) $4+-1$ (d) $-4+-3$ (e) $-2.5+1.5$
(f) $3.5+-1.5$ (g) $1.25-2.5$ (h) $3.75-1.5$. (i) $1-2.25$

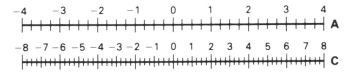

Fig. 7:2

18 Figure 7:2 can also be used for subtraction. Use the nomogram to find:
(a) $1--2$ (b) $1.5--1.75$ (c) $-0.25--2.75$

19 Design a nomogram for other expressions, e.g. $C = 2A + B$.

20 Investigate the symmetry of the answer table for question 16. What is the minimum number of calculations necessary to enable the table to be completed for three other values of x, y and z?

B Strings of + and −

For Discussion

$$-6 + 3 - 11 - 2 \rightarrow -3 - 11 - 2 \rightarrow -14 - 2 = -16$$

Using a Calculator

The above question needs the following key presses:

6 $\boxed{+/-}$ $\boxed{+}$ 3 $\boxed{-}$ 11 $\boxed{-}$ 2 $\boxed{=}$

Watch the display carefully as you key this in.

For questions 1 to 6 simplify the expressions to a single integer.

1 (a) $9 - 5 + 2$ (b) $8 - 3 - 2$ (c) $6 + 4 - 10$ (d) $5 + 6 - 1$ (e) $4 - 8 + 3$

2 (a) $7 - 1 - 6$ (b) $8 + 3 + 5$ (c) $-8 - 3 - 5$ (d) $-9 - 1 + 2$
    (e) $-8 - 2 + 11$ (f) $-16 + 2 + 18$

*3 (a) $6 + 3 + 4$ (b) $7 - 3 + 2$ (c) $7 - 2 + 3$ (d) $2 + 7 - 3$ (e) $2 + 3 - 7$

*4 (a) $7 + 5 - 12$ (b) $5 - 7 - 2$ (c) $5 - 2 - 7$ (d) $-5 - 2 - 7$ (e) $2 - 5 - 7$

5 (a) $4 + 1 + 8 + 6 + 5$ (b) $4 - 1 - 8 - 6 - 5$ (c) $-4 - 1 - 8 - 6 - 5$

6 (a) $4 - 1 - 8 + 6 + 5$ (b) $4 + 1 - 8 - 6 + 5$ (c) $4 - 1 - 8 - 6 + 5$

7 $(4-2)+6 = 2+6 = 8$ but $4-(2+6) = 4-8 = -4$

We can write this fact as: $(4-2)+6 \neq 4-(2+6)$.

Write each part of question 1 in two ways, using brackets and $=$ or $\neq$.

8 Rearrange the strings in question 1 in order of size.

For example, (a) $-5+2+9$.

9 **Example** $a-p+3d-2e$ can be rearranged in alphabetical order as $a+3d-2e-p$.

Rearrange in alphabetical order:
(a) $q+2a-w+z$ (b) $e-3c+a-2b$ (c) $-3d+a-4c-x$.

10 Simplify:
(a) $2x+1-x$ (b) $3x-x$ (c) $2+3a+1$ (d) $4x-x+2y$.

11 Simplify:
(a) $7a-2b-9a$ (b) $2x^2+3x^2$ (c) $5a^3+2a^3$ (d) $7a^2-5a^2$
(e) $6x^2y+2x^2y$.

12 Simplify:
(a) $3x^2+x+2x^2$ (b) $7a^2-9a-2a$ (c) $8xy^2+3xy+xy^2$.

13 Simplify, giving your answer with a positive term at the front, e.g. $3x-2a$ not $-2a+3x$, the expression:
(a) $7a-8a+c$ (b) $3c+2d-5c$ (c) $7-8+x^2+3x^2$ (d) $9x-x-12x+1$
(e) $3x^2y+2xy-4x^2y$ (f) $7xy-9xy+2xy^2$.

---

14 Write each part of questions 3 and 4 with brackets round the last two numbers.

(a) Work out each answer, e.g. $6+(3+4) = 6+7 = 13$.

(b) By investigating which answers in (a) are the same as the answers when there are no brackets, find a way to tell whether the answers are the same or different without working them out.

15 Find seven different answers to $7-6-3-4-1$ by using brackets.

16 Investigate the number of different answers possible for strings of different lengths to the one in question 15.

A Angles based on 60° bisection

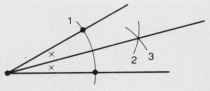

Fig. 8:1

To **bisect** means to cut into two equal parts.

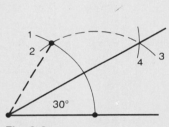

Fig. 8:2

A 30° angle may be constructed by bisecting a 60° angle.

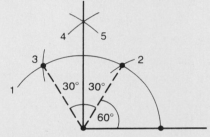

Fig. 8:3

A 90° angle may be constructed by a 30° angle joined to a 60° angle.

1 Draw five different angles in different positions. Bisect each of them.

2 Construct five angles of 30° at one end of each of five lines drawn at different slopes. The dotted lines as shown in Figure 8:2 need not be drawn.

3 Construct five angles of 90° at one end of each of five lines drawn at different slopes. The dotted lines as shown in Figure 8:3 need not be drawn.

4 Use angle bisection to construct the following angles. Explain briefly, as in Figures 8:2 and 8:3, how you constructed them.
(a) 15°   (b) 45°   (c) 75°   (d) 135°

5 Figure 8:4 illustrates a method for the construction of a rectangle. These are the steps:

I   Draw AB to the required length.

II Construct a 90° angle at A and mark D at the required distance.

III Centre B, draw an arc of radius equal to distance AD. Centre D, draw an arc of radius equal to distance AB. These arcs intersect at C.

IV Draw DC and BC.

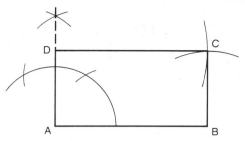

Fig. 8:4

Use this construction method for:
(a) a rectangle, sides 6 cm and 4 cm   (b) a rectangle, sides 5 cm and 3 cm
(c) a square, side 4 cm   (d) a square, side 6 cm.

6 Construct the quadrilaterals in Figure 8:5. Lengths are in centimetres. Use only a pair of compasses and a ruler. Be very neat.

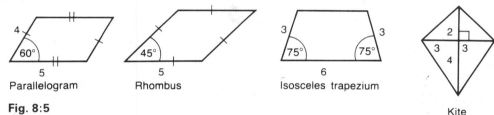

Parallelogram   Rhombus   Isosceles trapezium   Kite

Fig. 8:5

7 Draw five circles, each just touching both arms of one angle. Join their centres.

8 Construct Figure 8:6 accurately. ABCD is a square. DE bisects angle BDC.

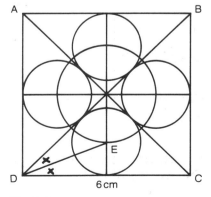

Fig. 8:6

9 Design a brooch to be made from interlocking silver wire.

B Triangles by 3 sides; inscribed circle

When a point moves it traces out a path called a **locus**.

If the point moves so that it is always a fixed distance from a fixed point, then the resulting locus is a circle, as shown in Figure 8:7.

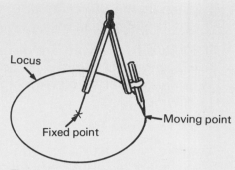

Fig. 8:7

Figure 8:8 shows a very complex locus drawn using a machine called a harmonograph. You may be able to draw a similar locus using your computer.

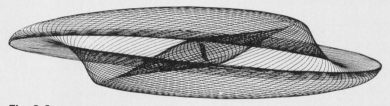

Fig. 8:8

1   Mark a point P, then draw the locus of a pencil point moving so that it is always 2 cm from P.

2   Mark two points, A and B, 4 cm apart. Use your compasses to draw the locus of *all* points 3 cm from A and *all* points $3\frac{1}{2}$ cm from B. Label X and Y, the two points that are both 3 cm from A *and* $3\frac{1}{2}$ cm from B. Draw triangle AXB and write on each side its length.

3   Figure 8:9 shows part of the diagram for question 2. It shows the method for the construction of △ABX, given that AB = 4 cm, AX = 3 cm and BX = $3\frac{1}{2}$ cm.

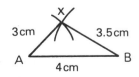

Fig. 8:9

Construct the following triangles, starting each time with side BC.
(a) BC = 10 cm, BA = 8 cm, CA = 6 cm   (b) BC = 6 cm, BA = 5 cm, CA = 4 cm
(c) BC = 6 cm, BA = CA = 5 cm   (d) BC = 7 cm, BA = CA = $4\frac{1}{2}$ cm

4 Write by each triangle you drew in question 3 its description, using one word from each of sets *A* and *S* where:
A = {acute-angled, obtuse-angled, right-angled}
S = {scalene, isosceles, equilateral}.

5 Figure 8:10 shows how to inscribe a circle in a triangle.

Bisect each angle of the triangles you drew for question 3, and hence draw the 'incircles'. Make sure that your circles just touch each side.

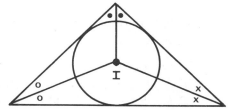
Fig. 8:10   An incircle

6 Construct △ABC with BC = 5 cm, AB = 2 cm and CA = 2.5 cm.

Comment on your 'triangle'.

7 Find which of the triangles in Figure 8:11 cannot be drawn to the sizes given.

(a)   (b)   (c)   (d)   (e)   (f)

Fig. 8:11

8 (a) Construct an equilateral triangle of side 8 cm. Label it ABC.

(b) Bisect each angle, making the bisectors reach the opposite sides.

(c) Let the bisector of angle A meet BC at D.

(d) Bisect ∠ADC. Let this bisector meet the bisector of ∠C at E.

(e) Set your compasses to the distance CE, then find points F on AD and G on the bisector of ∠B such that AF = BG = CE.

(f) Draw three circles, centres F, G and E, to fit exactly inside the triangle.

9 Find a construction like the one in question 8 for:
(a) 6 circles in a triangle
(b) 10 circles in a triangle.

C Perpendicular bisector; circumcircle

In Figure 8:12, XY is the **perpendicular bisector of AB**.

Perpendicular means 'at right angles to', so **a perpendicular bisector cuts in half at right angles.**

The locus of a point which is equidistant from two fixed points, A and B, is the perpendicular bisector of line AB.

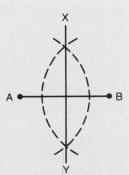

Fig. 8:12

1 Draw five lines at various slopes and construct the perpendicular bisector of each.

2 Construct the three triangles in Figure 8:13.

(a)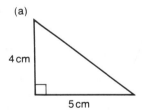

(b)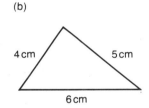

(c)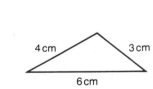

Fig. 8:13

3 Figure 8:14 shows how to construct the perpendicular bisectors of each side of a triangle.

(a) Construct the perpendicular bisector of each side of the triangles you drew in question 2. You may find it helps to turn the paper so that the line you are bisecting is horizontal.

(b) Using the point where the perpendicular bisectors cross as centre, draw the circles which pass through the three vertices (corners) of each triangle.

These are called the **circumcircles** of the triangles.

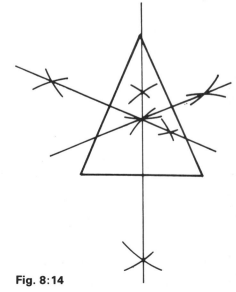

Fig. 8:14

4 Is the circumcentre (the centre of the circumcircle) inside or outside the triangle when the triangle is: (a) acute-angled (b) right-angled (c) obtuse-angled?

5

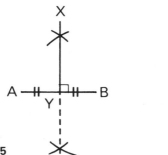

Fig. 8:15

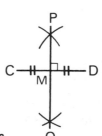

Fig. 8:16

(a) Construct Figure 8:15, where XY is the perpendicular bisector of AB. Make AB = 4 cm and XY = 4 cm.

(b) Construct Figure 8:16, where PQ is the perpendicular bisector of CD. Make CD = 4 cm, PM = 2 cm and QM = 2 cm.

(c) Repeat (b) when CD = 4 cm, PM = 4 cm and MQ = 4 cm.

(d) Repeat (b) when CD = 4 cm, PM = 2 cm and MQ = 4 cm.

6 (a) On your diagram for question 5(a), join A, X and B. What kind of a triangle have you drawn?

(b) On your diagram for question 5(b), join CPDQ. Name the resulting quadrilateral.

(c) Repeat (b) for diagrams 5(c) and 5(d). Exercise 8A question 6 will help you.

---

7 Construct and name the following loci. (Loci is the plural of locus.)

(a) A point keeping always a constant distance from a fixed point.

(b) A point keeping a constant distance from both arms of an angle.

(c) A point keeping a constant distance from both ends of a line.

8 Shade the following sets of points.

(a) More than 2 cm but less than 3 cm from a fixed point A.

(b) More than $2\frac{1}{2}$ cm but less than 4 cm from a fixed point B.

(c) Less than 4 cm from C and less than 3 cm from D where CD = 6 cm.

(d) Less than 3 cm from E and less than 2 cm from F where EF = 4 cm.

9 Draw designs based on all you have learnt in chapter 8.

9 Integers: negatives × and ÷

A Negative ×/÷ positive

For Discussion

In Figure 9:1 the upward journey from A to B is the positive (or +) direction. The downward journey from C to D is the negative (or −) direction.

The arcs on AB show that $5 \times +2 = +10$.

The arcs on CD show that $5 \times -2 = -10$.

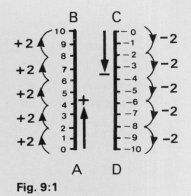

Fig. 9:1

Using a Calculator

5×-2 is entered as 5 $\boxed{\times}$ 2 $\boxed{+/-}$ $\boxed{=}$

Watch the display carefully as you key this in.

1 In Figure 9:2 the + direction is to the right and the − direction is to the left.

Copy Figure 9:2 and draw arcs:
(a) above the line to show $5 \times +2 = +10$
(b) below the line to show $5 \times -2 = -10$.

Fig. 9.2

2 Find:
(a) 4×2 (b) 4×-2 (c) 3×-6 (d) 4×-5 (e) 9×-10 (f) 9×-12.

3 A gardener picks 8 tomatoes a day for 7 days. Altogether he picks 56 tomatoes. We could say that he takes 8 (or -8) tomatoes every day and takes 56 (-56) altogether.

This story illustrates that $7 \times -8 = -56$.

Write a story to illustrate that $3 \times -6 = -18$.

4 You know that 2×3 has the same result as 3×2.

Similarly, 7×-8 and -8×7 both equal -56.

Find:
(a) 6×-8 (b) -8×6 (c) -7×7 (d) 8×-3 (e) 9×7 (f) -7×9.

46

5 Copy and complete these tables.

×	6	7	8	9
6	36			
7		49		63
8			64	
9				81

×	−6	−7	−8	−9
6				
7				
8				
9				

6 To find the answer to $63 \div 7$ we say 'How many sevens make 63?'
The answer is 9 because $9 \times 7 = 63$.

Similarly, to find $-63 \div 7$ we can say 'How many sevens make -63?'
The answer is -9 because $-9 \times 7 = -63$.

Again, to find $-63 \div -7$ we say 'How many times -7 is -63?'
The answer is 9 because $9 \times -7 = -63$.

Find:
(a) $36 \div 6$ (b) $-36 \div 6$ (c) $-42 \div 7$ (d) $48 \div 6$ (e) $-56 \div 7$
(f) $-36 \div -6$ (g) $-42 \div -7$ (h) $-48 \div -6$.

7 Find:
(a) $9 - -36$ (b) $-36 - 9$ (c) $36 - -9$ (d) $9 - 36$ (e) $-36 - -9$.

---

8 Imagine that you had to explain to a younger child what negative, or minus, numbers are. Write how you would do it and draw any pictures or diagrams that you would use to make it clear.

B Negative × negative

For Discussion

$3 \times -1 = -3$ (a) What should come after:
$2 \times -1 = -2$ (i) the 3, 2, 1, 0   (ii) the $-3, -2, -1, 0$?
$1 \times -1 = -1$
$0 \times -1 = 0$ (b) How should the pattern continue?

Example $-6 \times -3 = +18$ (or just 18)

Using a Calculator

The above example needs the following key presses.

6 $\boxed{+/-}$ $\boxed{\times}$ 3 $\boxed{+/-}$ $\boxed{=}$

Watch the display carefully as you key this in.

1 (a) -5×-4 (b) -4×-8 (c) -7×-3 (d) -4×-9 (e) 7×-5
(f) 6×-7 (g) -9×8 (h) -9×9 (i) -7×-7 (j) -10×-20

2 Example   To find $72 \div -8$.
Ask yourself 'How many times -8 is 72?'
The answer is -9, as $-9 \times -8 = 72$.

Find:
(a) $49 \div -7$ (b) $64 \div -8$ (c) $63 \div -7$ (d) $63 \div -9$ (e) $81 \div -9$.

3 Think very carefully about the following examples.

$6 + 3 = 9$	$-6 + 3 = -3$	$6 + -3 = 3$	$-6 + -3 = -9$
$6 - 3 = 3$	$-6 - 3 = -9$	$6 - -3 = 9$	$-6 - -3 = -3$
$6 \times 3 = 18$	$-6 \times 3 = -18$	$6 \times -3 = -18$	$-6 \times -3 = 18$
$6 \div 3 = 2$	$-6 \div 3 = -2$	$6 \div -3 = -2$	$-6 \div -3 = 2$

Learn the following rules.

Minus $\begin{array}{l}\text{times}\\\text{divide by}\end{array}$ **minus makes a plus.**

Minus minus makes plus. $(- - \rightarrow +)$

Plus $\begin{array}{l}\text{times}\\\text{divide by}\end{array}$ **minus makes a minus** *and* **Minus** $\begin{array}{l}\text{times}\\\text{divide by}\end{array}$ **plus makes a minus.**

Do *not* think of the first rule as 'Two minuses make a plus'. Two minuses *only* make a plus when they are multiplied or divided, for instance $-7 - 5$ is -12, not $+12$.

Find:
(a) 7×9 (b) -7×9 (c) 7×-9 (d) -7×-9 (e) $-7 - 9$ (f) $7 - 9$.

4 Check your answers to question 3 with a calculator. If you had any wrong, think about them again. Ask your teacher for help if necessary.

Then work out the answers to questions 5 to 10.

5 (a) 5×9 (b) $5 - 9$ (c) -5×9 (d) $-5 + 9$ (e) $-5 - 9$ (f) $9 - 5$

6 (a) 2×13 (b) -2×13 (c) $-2 + 13$ (d) $-2 - 13$ (e) -2×-13
     (f) $2 - 13$

7 (a) 4×15 (b) -4×-15 (c) 4×-15 (d) $-4 - 15$ (e) $-4 + 15$
     (f) $15 - 4$

8 (a) 3×16 (b) $-3 - 16$ (c) $3 - 16$ (d) -3×16 (e) -3×-16

9 (a) $7 - 11$ (b) -7×11 (c) -7×-11 (d) $-7 - 11$ (e) $-6 - 12$

10 (a) $12 - -4$ (b) $12 \div -4$ (c) $-12 \div -4$ (d) $-12 \div 4$

11 Check your answers to question 10 with a calculator. If you had any wrong, think about them again. Ask your teacher for help if necessary.

Then work out the answers to questions 12 to 15.

12 (a) $15 - -3$ (b) $15 \div -3$ (c) $-15 \div -3$ (d) $-15 \div 3$

13 (a) $20 \div -4$ (b) $-20 \div 4$ (c) $-20 \div -4$ (d) $-20 - 4$ (e) $20 - -4$

14 (a) $49 - 7$ (b) $-49 - 7$ (c) $-49 - -7$ (d) $-49 \div -7$ (e) $49 \div -7$

15 (a) $\dfrac{-18}{6}$ (b) $\dfrac{-18}{-6}$ (c) $\dfrac{18}{-6}$ (d) $-18 - 6$

16 You may use a calculator in this question, although it is probably quicker to work in your head.

If $a = -1$, $b = 2$, $c = -4$ and $d = -6$, find the value of:

(a) $a + b$ (b) $a - b$ (c) ab (d) $-a$ (e) $b - a$ (f) $\dfrac{b}{a}$

(g) $-b + a$ (h) $-b - a$ (i) b^2 (j) a^2 (k) $a + c$ (l) $a - c$

(m) ac (n) c^2 (o) $\dfrac{c}{b}$ (p) $c - b$ (q) bc (r) $c + d$ (s) $c - d$

(t) $d - c$ (u) $-c$ (v) $-c - d$ (w) $\dfrac{d}{b}$ (x) $a^2 b$ (y) bc^2 (z) ad^2

17 Draw a chart, or a series of charts, to illustrate attractively the rules of arithmetic with positive and negative integers.

10 Area: triangle

A Area of a triangle

For Discussion

Figure 10:1 shows that the area of a triangle is half the area of the rectangle into which it fits.

The area of the rectangle is $b \times h$, so the area of the triangle is $\frac{1}{2} \times b \times h$.

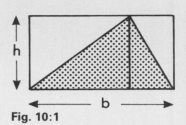

Fig. 10:1

This is usually remembered as:
The area of a triangle is half the base times the height.

What is the area of each triangle in Figure 10:2?

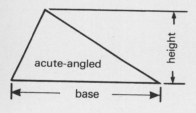

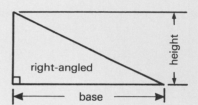

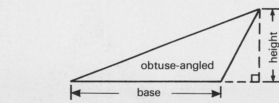

Fig. 10:2

1 Measure the base and height of each triangle in Figure 10:3 and so calculate its area in cm².

(a) 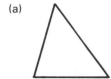 (b)   (c)

Fig. 10:3

2 Calculate: (a) $\frac{1}{2} \times 16 \times 9$ (b) $\frac{1}{2} \times 12 \times 10$ (c) $\frac{1}{2} \times 19 \times 20$ (d) $\frac{1}{2} \times 13 \times 9$.

3 Measure the base and height of each triangle in Figure 10:4 and so calculate its area in cm².

(a)
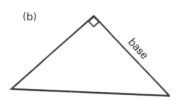

(b)
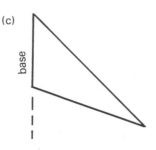

(c)
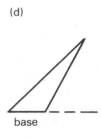

(d)

Fig. 10:4

*4 Measure the base and height of each triangle in Figure 10:5 and so calculate its area in cm².

(a)
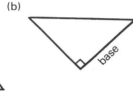

(b)
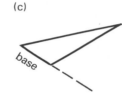

(c)

(d)
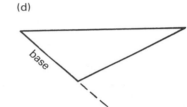

Fig. 10.5

5 For Figure 10:6 calculate the area of:
(a) the whole sign
(b) the inside triangle
(c) the coloured border.

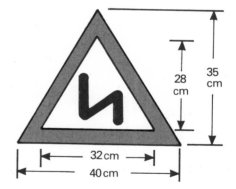

Fig. 10:6

With your teacher's permission you may use a calculator in the following questions.

6 (a) Construct △ABC with AB the horizontal line and:
  (i) AB = 4 cm, BC = 5 cm, AC = 8 cm   (ii) AB = 6 cm, BC = AC = 5 cm
  (iii) AB = 6 cm, ∠A = 60°, AC = 3.5 cm   (iv) AB = 4 cm, ∠B = 45°, AC = 4 cm.

(b) Measure the vertical height of each triangle and so calculate its area.

(c) On each triangle draw the altitude from point B to the side AC as base. Measure each altitude to the nearest millimetre and re-calculate the area using base AC.

51

10

7 Calculate (a) to (e) for each triangle in this table.

Base	6 cm	(b)	14 cm	(d)	$11\frac{1}{2}$ m
Altitude	(a)	8 cm	(c)	9 m	(e)
Area	24 cm²	32 cm²	49 cm²	54 m²	46 m²

8 Calculate the length of the altitude to the longest side in a right-angled triangle with sides 5 cm, 12 cm and 13 cm.

9 Investigate the areas of triangles made with a continuous loop of string 20 cm long. What shape triangle has the largest area?

B   Areas of compound shapes

Figure 10:7 shows a speed/time graph.

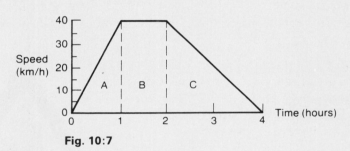

Fig. 10:7

The area under the graph gives the distance travelled.

To find this area it has been divided into three sections:

Area of triangle A $= \frac{1}{2} \times 1 \times 40 = 20$
Area of rectangle B $= 1 \times 40 = 40$
Area of triangle C $= \frac{1}{2} \times 2 \times 40 = 40$

Total area $= 100$

The distance travelled is 100 km.

1 Sketch the diagrams in Figure 10:8 (not exactly), then calculate their areas by dividing them into triangles and rectangles.

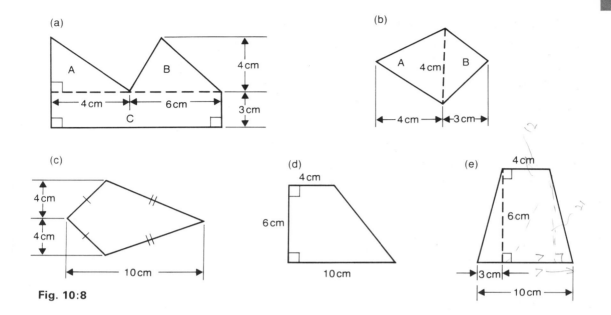

Fig. 10:8

With your teacher's permission you may use a calculator for the following questions.

2 Sketch a right-angled triangle with sides 3.75 cm, 5 cm and 6.25 cm. Calculate its area and the area of a triangle whose sides are twice as long. Comment on the connection between your two answers.

3 Figure 10:9 shows a design for some roof rafters. Angle ACB is to be a right angle, AC is 3 m, BC is 4 m and AB is 5 m (all measurements are approximate).

By finding the area of △ABC in two ways find the approximate length of the vertical support.

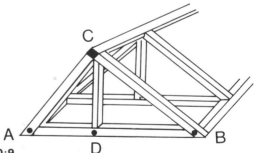

Fig. 10:9

4 A triangle has a base of 3.4 m and a height of 2.65 m.

(a) Calculate its area in m².

(b) Convert the base and height to cm and so calculate the area in cm².

(c) Compare your answers to (a) and (b). Explain how to convert from m² to cm² and from cm² to m².

5 Change to cm²:
(a) 1 m²   (b) 3 m²   (c) 3.5 m²   (d) 3.56 m²   (e) 12.1 m².

6 Change to m²: (a) 310 000 cm²   (b) 716 000 cm²   (c) 85 000 cm².

7 Areas of irregular fields are often found by marking out a straight line across the field, then measuring from this line, as shown in Figure 10:10.

The measurements are recorded in a special table.

(a) Using a scale of 1:1000 draw a plan of the field in Figure 10:10. Start with the line AD (100 m → 10 cm). Remember to state the scale on your diagram.

(b) Calculate the area of the field. It helps if you write the true lengths of the lines on your diagram.

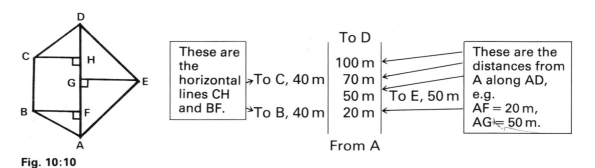

Fig. 10:10

8 Using a scale of 1:1000 draw a plan of the field represented by this table.

Calculate its area.

```
                          To C
                          120 m
                           96 m    To D, 41 m
              To B, 35 m   60 m
                           40 m    To E, 58 m
                          From A
```

---

9 On a thick piece of paper draw a net (the flat shape that folds to make a solid model) for an Egyptian pyramid.

The base is to be a square of side 3.5 cm and the equal sides of the triangles are to be 4.5 cm.

Calculate the area of the net and make the pyramid.

10 Find the area of an irregular shape using the method of question 7. Can you find a better method? Write about it.

11 Relations: mappings; graphs

A Mappings and inequalities

$x \neq y$ means x is not equal to y.
$x < y$ means x is less than y.
$x < y$ also means y is more than x.
$x \leqslant y$ means x is equal to y or is less than y.
$x \leqslant y$ also means y is equal to x or is more than x.

Example If $x \in \{-2, -1, 0, 1, 2\}$ and $-1 \leqslant x < 1$ then x can only be -1 or 0.

1 If $x \in \{-5, -4, -3, -2, -1, 0, 1, 2, 3, 4, 5\}$ list the set:
  (a) $\{x : 2 < x \leqslant 5\}$ (b) $\{x : -3 < x < 1\}$ (c) $\{x : -4 < x \leqslant 0\}$
  (d) $\{x : -1 < x \leqslant 1\}$ (e) $\{x : -2 \leqslant x \leqslant 1\}$ (f) $\{x : -3 < x < -1\}$.

2 The relation diagram illustrates the mapping $x \rightarrow 2x$

You will often find this written as $f : x \rightarrow 2x$.

Read it as **'A function of x is such that x maps onto $2x$'.**

Domain	Range
$x \longrightarrow 2x$	
$1 \longrightarrow 2$	
$0 \longrightarrow 0$	
$-1 \longrightarrow -2$	
$-2 \longrightarrow -4$	

Using the same domain draw relation diagrams to illustrate:
  (a) $f : x \rightarrow 3x$ (b) $f : x \rightarrow x + 1$ (c) $f : x \rightarrow x - 3$ (d) $f : x \rightarrow 2x + 2$.

3 Draw relation diagrams for integral values of x to illustrate:

  (a) $f : x \rightarrow 3x - 4$ for $1 < x \leqslant 5$ (b) $f : x \rightarrow x^2$ for $-4 < x < 1$
  (c) $f : x \rightarrow x^2 + 3$ for $-1 < x < 4$ (d) $f : x \rightarrow -2x$ for $-3 \leqslant x \leqslant 1$
  (e) $f : x \rightarrow -2x + 1$ for $-2 \leqslant x < 3$ (f) $f : x \rightarrow -3x - 2$ for $-3 < x < 3$.

---

4 In this question $p * q$ means 'Carry out the mapping q first, then use the image so found to carry out the mapping p.'

Example If $x = 2$, $p : x \rightarrow x + 1$ and $q : x \rightarrow 2x$,

Then $p * q$ gives $2 \xrightarrow{q} 4$ and $4 \xrightarrow{p} 5$.

Answer $2 \xrightarrow{p*q} 5$.

And $q * p$ gives $2 \xrightarrow{p} 3$ and $3 \xrightarrow{q} 6$.

Answer $2 \xrightarrow{q*p} 6$.

Find $p * q$ and $q * p$ where $p : x \rightarrow x + 1$ and $q : x \rightarrow 2x$ for:
  (a) $x = 3$ (b) $x = -7$.

5 If $x \in \{-3, -2, 0, 2\}$ list the sets formed by (i) $q*p$ and (ii) $p*q$ if:
(a) $p: x \to x - 3$ and $q: x \to 3x$ (b) $p: x \to x - 2$ and $q: x \to -2x$
(c) $p: x \to x^2$ and $q: x \to 2x$ (d) $p: x \to 2x$ and $q: x \to x^3$.

B   From a mapping to a graph

For Discussion

$f: x \to x + 1$

As a mapping:	As co-ordinates:	As a graph:
$x \to x + 1$	$(\quad x, \quad y)$	
$-2 \to -1$	$(-2, -1)$	
$-1 \to \quad 0$	$(-1, \quad 0)$	
$0 \to \quad 1$	$(\quad 0, \quad 1)$	
$1 \to \quad 2$	$(\quad 1, \quad 2)$	
$2 \to \quad 3$	$(\quad 2, \quad 3)$	

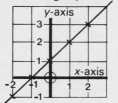

1 Using $x \in \{x: -2 \leqslant x \leqslant 2\}$ show as a mapping, as co-ordinates, and as a graph:
(a) $x \to x + 2$ (b) $x \to x - 2$ (c) $x \to 4x$.

*2 Write as a mapping, as co-ordinates, and as a graph:
(a) $x \to x + 3$ where $x \in \{x: -5 \leqslant x \leqslant 0\}$ (b) $x \to 3y$ where $x \in \{x: -2 \leqslant x \leqslant 2\}$.

3 Draw a graph for the mapping:
(a) $x \to -x + 2$ for $-2 \leqslant x \leqslant 2$ (b) $x \to -x - 2$ for $-2 \leqslant x \leqslant 2$
(c) $x \to x$ for $-2 \leqslant x \leqslant 2$ (d) $x \to 2x - 1$ for $-3 \leqslant x \leqslant 2$
(e) $x \to 2x + 3$ for $-4 \leqslant x \leqslant 1$ (f) $x \to 3x + 3$ for $-3 \leqslant x \leqslant 2$.

4 The mapping $x \to x + 1$ can be written as the relation $x \xrightarrow{\text{add 1}} y$, giving the equation $y = x + 1$.

Similarly $x \to x - 4$ becomes $y = x - 4$.

Write the equations for the mappings in question 1.

5 For values of x from -3 to 3 draw the graph of:
(a) $y = 3 - x$ (b) $y = x - 1$ (c) $y = -x - 1$ (d) $y = x^2$ (e) $y = x^3$.

12 Algebra: simplification; formulae

A Simplification

Like terms have the same letters and the same powers of those letters.

Like terms can be added and subtracted. Unlike terms cannot.

Any two terms can be multiplied to make one term.

Examples $3ky^2$ and ky^2 are like terms.

$3ky^2$ and ky and $3k$ are unlike terms.

$3ky^2 + ky - ky^2 = 2ky^2 + ky$

$3k \times ky = 3k^2y$

1 Simplify:
(a) $d + d + d$ (b) $a \times a \times a$ (c) $2x + 3x$ (d) $4x - 2x + 3x$
(e) $7a + 5 - 2a$ (f) $4a - 6 - 3a$ (g) $2x + 3y + 5x - 2y$ (h) $2 + 3x$.

2 State the unlike term in the set:
(a) $\{2xy, 2x, 3xy\}$ (b) $\{4ab, ab, 4a\}$ (c) $\{3x^2, 2x^2, 3\}$
(d) $\{5x^2, 5a^2, x^2\}$ (e) $\{2x^2y, 2xy, 7x^2y\}$.

3 **Example**   The sum of the elements of $\{7a^2b, 3ab, 2a^2b\}$ is
$7a^2b + 3ab + 2a^2b = 9a^2b + 3ab$.

Write the sums of the elements of the sets in question 2.

4 Simplify if possible:
(a) $x^2 + 3x^2 + 5x^2$ (b) $x^2 + 7x^2 + x$ (c) $5a^2b + 3ab + 2a^2b$ (d) $7x^2 - x^2$
(e) $4a^2 - a^2$ (f) $5a^2b - b$.

5 Simplify if possible:
(a) $2x + 3x - 5x$ (b) $4a^2 - 2a^2 - 2a^2$ (c) $4x + 6x - 8$ (d) $5xy + 3x^2y - 1$
(e) $4p^2 - p^2 - p^3$ (f) $2x^2y + 8x^2y - 3x^2$.

*6 Simplify:
(a) $x^2 + 2x^2$ (b) $3x^2 + 2x^2$ (c) $5x^2 - 2x^2$ (d) $7x^2 - 6x^2$ (e) $xy + xy$.

*7 Simplify:
(a) $3xy - xy$ (b) $4xy + 2xy + xy$ (c) $7x^2y + x^2y$ (d) $8x + 3y + 2x$.

57

*8 Simplify:
(a) $8x^2 + 3y + 2x^2$ (b) $8x^2 + 3y - 2x^2$ (c) $8xy^2 - 2x + 2xy^2$
(d) $8xy^2 - 2x + 2x$ (e) $3x + x^2 + 2x$.

9 Most of the following simplifications are wrong. Write correct expressions for the wrong ones. (The $\equiv$ sign is the identity sign. It is used for two expressions which have identical values when numbers are substituted for the letters.)

(a) $2x + x \equiv 2x^2$ (b) $3x - x \equiv 3$ (c) $4 + 2x \equiv 6x$ (d) $7x + 3x \equiv 10x$
(e) $5x + y \equiv 5xy$ (f) $x^2 + y^2 \equiv x^2y^2$ (g) $7x^2 - x^2 \equiv 7$
(h) $4p^2 + 3p + p \equiv 8p^2$ (i) $4p^2 + 3p + p \equiv 7p^2$ (j) $4p^2 - p^2 + p \equiv 3p^2 + p$
(k) $3x + 2y - y \equiv 3x + 2$

10 Under the mapping $f{:}x \to x^2 + x$ any given value of x is squared then added to the given value.

Example $f(3) = 3^2 + 3 = 9 + 3 = 12$

Find for the mapping $f{:}x \to x^2 + x$ the value of:
(a) $f(5)$ (b) $f(7)$ (c) $f(13)$ (d) $f(25)$.

11 Find for the mapping $f{:}x \to x^3 + 2x$ the value of:
(a) $f(1)$ (b) $f(2)$ (c) $f(3)$ (d) $f(4)$ (e) $f(5)$.

---

12 Copy and complete the following by writing the mapping on the arrow lines.

Example $x^2 \xrightarrow{+y} x^2 + y \xrightarrow{+2x^2} 3x^2 + y$

(a) $a \longrightarrow a + b \longrightarrow 2a + b$ (b) $c^2 \longrightarrow c^2 + 2d \longrightarrow c^2 + d$

(c) $x^2 \longrightarrow x^2 + 8b \longrightarrow x^2 + 3b$ (d) $c \longrightarrow c^2 \xrightarrow{\times} 2c^2$

(e) $g \longrightarrow g^2 \xrightarrow{\times} 3g^2$ (f) $h \xrightarrow{+} 3h \longrightarrow 3h^2$

(g) $k \xrightarrow{\times} 2k \xrightarrow{\times} 6k$ (h) $m \xrightarrow{+} 2m \xrightarrow{+} 6m$

(i) $n \longrightarrow n + 6 \longrightarrow 6$

13 **Example** $3(x + 6) \to 3x + 18$

Note: Both the x and the 6 have been multiplied by 3.

Remove the bracket from:
(a) $2(x + 4)$ (b) $2(x + 5)$ (c) $3(x + 9)$ (d) $8(x + 7)$ (e) $x(x + 1)$
(f) $x(x + 3)$ (g) $x(x + 7)$ (h) $x(x^2 + 3)$.

B Formulae

Light travels nearly a million times faster than sound, which is why you hear the thunder after you see the lightning flash.

If the time between the flash and the clap of thunder is t seconds then the thundercloud is about a third of t kilometres away.

We can write this briefly in a formula, $d = \dfrac{t}{3}$,

where t is the time in seconds and d is the distance in kilometres.

If the time between flash and clap is 5 seconds then the thundercloud is $\dfrac{5}{3} = 1\frac{2}{3}$ km away.

Fig. 12:1

1   The area of a rectangle is found by multiplying its length by its width. This can be written as the formula: $A = lw$, where A is the area, l is the length and w is the width.

Find the value of A if:
(a) $l = 6$ cm, $w = 3$ cm   (b) $l = 8$ cm, $w = 7$ cm   (c) $l = 9$ cm, $w = 8$ cm
(d) $l = 35$ cm, $w = 28$ cm.

2   The formula for the area of a square is $A = s^2$, where s is the length of the side.

Find the area of a square with side:
(a) 4 cm   (b) 7 cm   (c) 11 cm   (d) 1.5 cm.

3   The formula for the perimeter of a rectangle is $P = 2l + 2w$, where l and w are its length and width. Find the value of P for the rectangles in question 1.

4   The formula for the perimeter of a square is $P = 4s$, where s is the length of a side. Find the value of P for the squares in question 2.

5   The formula for the perimeter of a regular pentagon is $P = 5s$, where s is the length of a side.

Write a formula for the perimeter of:
(a) an equilateral triangle   (b) a square   (c) a regular hexagon
(d) a regular octagon.

6 The perimeter of the shape in Figure 12:2 is given by the formula

$$P = a + b + a + b + 2a + 2b \xrightarrow{\text{becomes}} P = 4a + 4b.$$

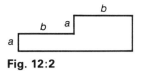

Fig. 12:2

Find the perimeter formula for each shape in Figure 12:3.

(a)   (b)   (c)   (d)

Isosceles triangle

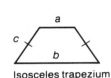

Isosceles trapezium

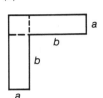

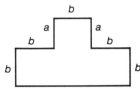

Fig. 12:3

7 At s km/h a car travels d km in t hours, where $t = d \div s$.

Find the time taken to travel:
(a) 40 km at 20 km/h   (b) 60 km at 20 km/h   (c) 50 km at 30 km/h.

8 The area of a circle is given by $A = 3.1 \times r^2$, where r is the radius.

Find the area of a circle with radius:
(a) 3 cm   (b) 4 cm   (c) 5 cm   (d) 10 cm.

9 A car travelling at s km/h can, in an emergency, usually stop in d metres, where $d = \dfrac{s^2}{200} + \dfrac{s}{5}$.

Example At 20 km/h the car can stop in
$$\frac{20^2}{200} + \frac{20}{5} = \frac{400}{200} + 4 = 2 + 4 = 6 \text{ m}.$$

Find the stopping distance at:
(a) 40 km/h   (b) 60 km/h   (c) 80 km/h   (d) 10 km/h.

10 The volume of a cube of side s cm is given by $V = s^3$. Use your calculator to help you find the side of a 100 cm³ cube correct to 3 decimal places. (Hint: Find the value of s that gives V somewhere near 100, then use 'trial and improvement' to steadily improve the accuracy of s.)

11 Check the following area formulae by drawing the shapes on 1 cm-squared paper and counting squares.

(a) Triangle: $A = \dfrac{bh}{2}$ where $b =$ length of base and $h =$ height.

(b) Parallelogram (Figure 12:4): $A = bh$

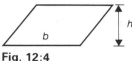

Fig. 12:4

(c) Trapezium (Figure 12:5):
$A = \frac{1}{2}(a + b) \times h$

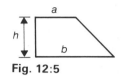

Fig. 12:5

(d) Rhombus (Figure 12:6): $A = \dfrac{xy}{2}$ where x and y are the lengths of the dotted lines.

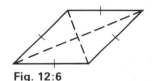

Fig. 12:6

12 Draw an ellipse (Figure 12:7) using a loop of string and two 'point-up' drawing pins. Check the area formula $A = 3.14 (s + t)$.

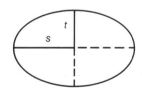

Fig. 12:7

13 Illustrate by a graph, or otherwise, the change in stopping distance as speed increases, using the formula in question 9.

14 A useful rule to gauge whether a driver is keeping a safe distance behind the vehicle in front is the 'two second rule'.

If you have time to say 'Only a fool ignores the two second rule' (which takes about two seconds to say) between the vehicle in front passing a lamp-post and you reaching the same post, then you are a safe distance behind.

Investigate what safe distances vehicles should keep between them at different speeds.

15 Find some formulae and write about how they are used.

13 Graphs: lines; regions

A Equations of lines parallel to axes

For Discussion

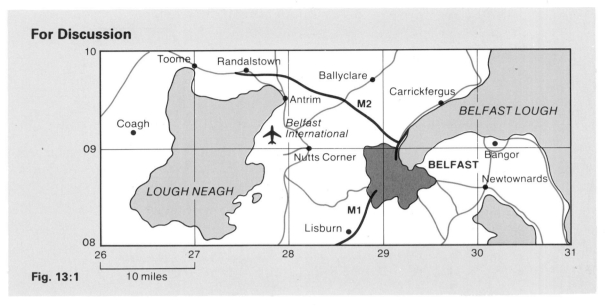

Fig. 13:1   10 miles

1 For Figure 13:2

(a) Write the co-ordinates of points A to H.

(b) Name the point (0, 0).

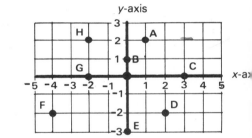

Fig. 13:2

2 Copy the axes in Figure 13:2, but not the lettered points. 1 cm-squared paper is recommended.

(a) Plot: (5, 1); (4, 1); (3, 1); (2, 1); (1, 1); (0, 1); (− 1, 1); (− 2, 1); (− 3, 1); (− 4, 1); (− 5, 1).

Join the points, using a ruler.

(b) State the co-ordinates of five more points on the same line.

(c) All the points share the common value $y = 1$.

$y = 1$ is the equation of the line you drew. Write $y = 1$ on it, near one 'end'.

(d) Does $y = 1$ really have an end? Is (369, 1) a point on $y = 1$?

(e) On the same axes join (− 5, 2) to (5, 2). Write the equation of this line on it.

(f) Draw and label the lines $y = 3$, $y = − 1$ and $y = − 3$.

(g) Write the co-ordinates of five points on the x-axis.

(h) What is the equation of the x-axis? Write this equation on it.

3 Draw and label axes, *x* from − 5 to 5, *y* from − 3 to 3.

Write '*x*-axis, *y* = 0' on the horizontal axis.

(a) Plot (3, 3), (3, 1) and (3, − 3). Join them, using a ruler.

(b) Name five more points on the same line.

(c) All the points share the common value *x* = 3.
   x = 3 is the equation of the line you drew. Write *x* = 3 at one 'end' of it.

(d) Draw and label the lines: *x* = 5; *x* = 2; *x* = − 1; *x* = − 3; *x* = − 5.

(e) What value has *x* along the *y*-axis? Write the equation of the *y*-axis at one 'end'.

4 In Figure 13:2, A is the intersection (crossing point) of two lines parallel to the axes; it lies on *x* = 1 going 'up' and on *y* = 2 going across.

Name the *two* lines parallel to the axes on which the following lie:
(a) D   (b) F   (c) H   (d) E   (e) G.

*5 What is the equation of: (a) the *x*-axis   (b) the *y*-axis?

*6 Draw axes as in question 3. Label the axes '*x*-axis, *y* = 0' and '*y*-axis, *x* = 0'.

Plot the following pairs of points and join each pair with a straight line, writing the equation of each line at the 'end' of it.
(a) (4, − 3) and (4, 1)   (b) (5, − 2) and (5, 3)   (c) (2, − 3) and (1, − 3)

*7 Without plotting the points, write the equation of the line which passes through:
(a) (7, − 2) and (7, − 5)   (b) (9, − 3) and (9, 3)   (c) (4, − 8) and (6, − 8)
(d) (− 7, − 2) and (7, − 2)   (e) (0, 4) and (0, 5)   (f) (3, 0) and (0, 0).

*8 In Figure 13:2, name the two grid lines on which point B lies.

9 Write the co-ordinates of the crossing point of the lines:
(a) *x* = 5 and *y* = − 3   (b) *x* = − 2 and *y* = − 7   (c) *y* = − 4 and *x* = − 2 (careful!)
(d) *y* = 4 and *y* = 3 (think!).

10 **A**: none; **B**: one; **C**: four; **D**: ten; **E**: a hundred; **F**: a thousand; **G**: an infinite number.

Choose answer A, B, C, D, E, F, or G for the answer to:
How many points are there on the line *x* = 4 between *y* = 2 and *y* = 3?

11 {(*x*, *y*):*x* = 3} is read as 'The set of points on a graph such that *x* equals 3'. It is the line *x* = 3. What is {(*x*, *y*):*x* = 3} ∩ {(*x*, *y*):*y* = 2}?

12 Your answer to question 11 should have been 'The point (3, 2)'.

Remember that ∩ is the intersection of the two sets; the point on $x = 3$ that is also on $y = 2$. Only (3, 2) fits this requirement.

Write in set notation, using the ∩ sign, the following points as the intersection of two lines.
(a) $(-3, 0)$ (b) $(-2, -1)$ (c) the origin

13 (a) Draw axes, x from -6 to 6, y from -3 to 3. (5 or 6 mm-squared paper is best for this question.)

Plot $(-4, -3)$, $(-3, 1)$ and $(-2, -3)$. Join them to make a triangle.

(b) Reflect the triangle, using $x = 0$ as the mirror line.

Write the co-ordinates of the vertices (corners) of the image.

14 Repeat question 13(a) then repeat 13(b) *but* use $x = 1$ as the mirror line.

15 Repeat question 13(a) and (b) but use $y = 0$ as the mirror line.

16 Repeat question 13(a) and (b) but use $y = -1$ as the mirror line.

17 (a) Draw axes as in question 13(a).

Plot $(-4, -3)$, $(-1, -3)$, $(-3, -2)$ and $(-2, -2)$.

Join these points to make a quadrilateral (an isosceles trapezium).

(b) Reflect the isosceles trapezium in $y = -1$ and in $x = -1$.

Write the co-ordinates of the image as a mapping.

Example   When reflected in $y = -1$:
$(-4, -3) \rightarrow (-4, 1)$; $(-1, -3) \rightarrow (-1, 1)$; etc.

---

18 State the mirror lines for the following reflections. Do it without plotting the points if you can.

(a) $(-3, 2) \rightarrow (3, 2)$ (b) $(5, 1) \rightarrow (-5, 1)$ (c) $(3, -2) \rightarrow (3, 2)$
(d) $(2, 6) \rightarrow (2, 0)$ (e) $(4, -2) \rightarrow (0, -2)$ (f) $(-3, 5) \rightarrow (-3, 1)$
(g) $(-6, -3) \rightarrow (-6, 5)$ (h) $(2, 0) \rightarrow (2, 0)$ Note: (h) has many answers.

19 Investigate the change in the co-ordinates of a point when it is reflected in $x = 0$ and $y = 0$. Write about your findings. Then extend your investigation to reflection in other lines.

B Regions

Example Shade the set of points given by
$\{(x, y): -1 < x < 2\} \cap \{(x, y): -1 < y < 1\}$

From the sets we can see that the lines to be drawn are $x = -1$, $x = 2$, $y = -1$ and $y = 1$.

Figure 13:3 shows the finished answer.

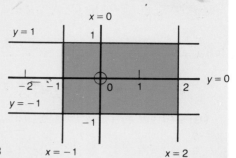

Fig. 13:3

1 Draw and label six sets of axes from -3 to 3 each.

Answer one of the following parts on each grid.

Draw and label:

(a) $x = 1$; hatch /// the region $x > 1$ (b) $x = -2$; hatch /// the region $x > -2$
(c) $x = 3$; hatch /// the region $x < 3$ (d) $y = -1$; hatch \\\ the region $y < -1$
(e) $y = 2$; hatch \\\ the region $y > 2$ (f) $y = -2$; hatch \\\ the region $y < -2$.

2 Draw and label four sets of axes from -3 to 3 each.

Answer one of the following parts on each grid.

(a) Hatch /// $\{(x, y): -3 < x < 0\}$ (b) Hatch \\\ $\{(x, y): -3 < y < -1\}$

(c) Shade ■ $\{(x, y): 1 < x < 2\} \cap \{(x, y): 1 < y < 2\}$

(d) Shade ▨ $\{(x, y): -2 < x < 0\} \cap \{(x, y): -3 < y < -1\}$

*3 In Figure 13:4, which of points A to F are in the following regions? (There will usually be more than one point in your answer.)

(a) $x > 1$ (b) $x < 1$ (c) $x < -2$
(d) $x > 0$ (e) $x < 0$ (f) $y > 1$
(g) $y < 1$ (h) $y > -2$ (i) $y < -2$
(j) $y > 0$ (k) $y < 0$ (l) $-2 < x < 1$
(m) $-2 < y < 0$
(n) $\{(x, y): -2 < x < 1\} \cap \{(x, y): -2 < y < 1\}$

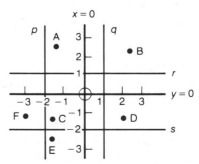

Fig. 13:4

*4 Draw and label four sets of axes from -4 to 4 each.

Answer one of the following parts on each of your grids.

(a) Hatch ///: $\{(x, y): 2 < x < 4\}$ (b) Hatch \\\\: $\{(x, y): -4 < y < 1\}$

(c) Shade ■: $\{(x, y): -3 < x < 0\} \cap \{(x, y): 1 < y < 4\}$

(d) Shade ■: $\{(x, y): 1 < x < 4\} \cap \{(x, y): -4 < y < 0\}$

5   $A = \{(x, y): x < 2\}$ $B = \{(x, y): x > -2\}$
    $C = \{(x, y): y > -1\}$ $D = \{(x, y): y < 2\}$

On axes from -3 to 3, using one set of axes for each part, hatch or shade:
(a) $A \cap B$ (b) $C \cap D$ (c) $(A \cap B) \cap (C \cap D)$ (d) $A \cap C$
(e) $A \cap D$ (f) $B \cap C$ (g) $B \cap D$ (h) $(A \cap C) \cap (B \cap D)$.

6   On axes from -3 to 3 plot $(-3, -3)$, $(0, 0)$ and $(3, 3)$.

Join them with a straight line. Why is the equation of this line $y = x$?

Shade the region $y > x$.

Which of the following are:
(a) on $y = x$ (b) in the region $y > x$ (c) in the region $y < x$?

A: $(2, 3)$;   B: $(3, 2)$;   C: $(-1, 0)$;   D: $(-3, 1)$;   E: $(-2, -1)$;   F: $(-2, -3)$;
G: $(-3, -3)$;   H: $(-4, -7)$;   I: $(-7, -4)$;   J: $(11, 34)$;   K: $(-38, -36)$;
L: $(100, 100)$

7   On three sets of axes from -3 to 3 hatch or shade the region:

(a) $\{(x, y): y > x\} \cap \{(x, y): -1 < x < 2\}$ (b) $\{x, y): y > x\} \cap \{(x, y): -2 < y < 0\}$

(c) $\{(x, y): y > x\} \cap \{(x, y): -1 < x < 2\} \cap \{(x, y): -2 < y < 1\}$

8   For the line $y = -x$ the y co-ordinate must be minus the x co-ordinate, e.g. $(-3, 3)$ is on $y = -x$ because $3 = --3$.

Complete so that they are also points on $y = -x$ the co-ordinates: $(-1,\ )$; $(1,\ )$; $(3,\ )$.

Does $(0, 0)$ lie on $y = -x$?

On four sets of axes from -3 to 3 hatch or shade the region:

(a) $\{(x, y): y > -x\} \cap \{(x, y): -1 < x < 2\}$

(b) $\{(x, y): y < -x\} \cap \{(x, y): -1 < x < 2\} \cap \{(x, y): -3 < y < 1\}$

(c) $\{(x, y): y > -x\} \cap \{(x, y): -2 < x < -1\} \cap \{(x, y): 0 < y < 3\}$

(d) $\{(x, y): y > -x\} \cap \{(x, y): y > x\} \cap \{(x, y): y < 2\}$.

Project

The isosceles triangle

1 On a piece of card, construct accurately the isosceles triangle shown in Figure P1:1.

Cut it out carefully and *keep it* for use as a template to draw round.

Fig. P1:1

2 Cut out six isosceles triangles from gummed paper, using your template. By joining pairs of shapes make the three quadrilaterals shown in Figure P1:2.

Stick the shapes into your book or onto your project file-paper. Under each shape write its name. Then write sentences about each, saying all you can about its sides and its angles.

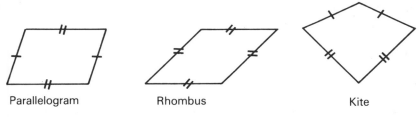

Parallelogram   Rhombus   Kite

Fig. P1:2

3 Repeat question 2 up to naming the shapes, then draw straight lines joining the corners of each shape (its diagonals).

Which quadrilaterals have:

(a) both diagonals the same length

(b) the diagonals crossing at right angles

(c) a diagonal bisected (cut in half) by another. Are both bisected?

4 Trace your three quadrilaterals. Cut out the tracing.

Which of your quadrilaterals:

(a) fold in half one way only

(b) fold in half two ways

(c) will not fold in half

(d) look the same upside down?

5 Use your template to cut out three isosceles triangles.

Stick them together to make an isosceles trapezium (Figure P1:3).

Write its name under it.

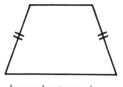

Isosceles trapezium

Fig. P1:3

6 Write about the sides and angles of an isosceles trapezium.

7 Repeat question 5, then draw the diagonals and write all you can about them.

8 Trace your isosceles trapezium and find out if it folds in half.

9 Use your template to cut out four isosceles triangles.

Stick them together to make one large isosceles triangle.

What can you say about the shape of the small and big triangles? Two shapes like this are said to be *similar*.

10 Use your template to cut out two more triangles. Fold one of the triangles in half and cut along the fold.

Stick the three pieces together to make a rectangle.

Write its name underneath and write all you can about the sides and angles of a rectangle.

11 Repeat question 10 up to naming the shape, then write all you can about the diagonals.

12 Cut out a tracing of the rectangle. How many ways can it be folded in half?

13 Cut out two more triangles. Cut one in half then stick the three pieces together to make a large right-angled triangle similar to one of the smaller ones.

14 On a piece of card construct accurately the right-angled isosceles triangle shown in Figure P1:4.

Cut it out and use it as a template to make two gummed-paper triangles. Join the pieces to make a square.

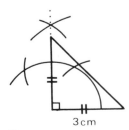

3 cm

Fig. P1:4

15 Write all you can about the sides, angles and diagonals of a square.

16 Cut out a tracing of the square and find how many ways it will fold in half.

17 Copy and complete the table in Figure P1:5 to summarise your findings from this project.

NAME	Number of pairs of parallel sides	Number of equal sides	Number of equal angles	Diagonals equal? Yes/No	Number of diagonals bisected	Diagonals cross at right angles? Yes/No	Number of ways of folding in half	Looks same upside down? Yes/No
Isosceles trapezium								
Kite								
Parallelogram		2 pairs						
Rhombus	2		2 pairs					
Rectangle								
Square		4						

Fig. P1:5

18 As extra experiments, start with the triangles in Figure P1:6 and investigate all the shapes you can make.

7cm
Obtuse-angled isosceles triangle

4 cm
Equilateral triangle

Fig. P1:6

14 Integers: review; problems

A novel way to subtract

$$\begin{array}{r} 2701 \\ -\ \underline{538} \end{array} \rightarrow \begin{array}{r} 2701 \\ \underline{0538} \end{array} \rightarrow \begin{array}{r} 2701 \\ 9461 \\ +\ \underline{\quad 1} \\ \underline{12163} \end{array} \quad \text{Answer } 2163.$$

$$\begin{array}{r} 10\,032 \\ -\ \underline{8\,906} \end{array} \rightarrow \begin{array}{r} 10\,032 \\ \underline{08\,906} \end{array} \rightarrow \begin{array}{r} 10\,032 \\ 91\,093 \\ +\ \underline{\quad 1} \\ \underline{101\,126} \end{array} \quad \text{Answer } 1126.$$

1 $316 + 29 + 708 + 4 + 1790$

2 $\begin{array}{r} 416 \\ -\ \underline{207} \end{array}$ **3** $\begin{array}{r} 29 \\ \times\ \underline{7} \end{array}$ **4** $\begin{array}{r} 38 \\ \times\ \underline{20} \end{array}$ **5** $\begin{array}{r} 46 \\ \times\ \underline{89} \end{array}$

6 $8620 \div 4$ **7** $71\,600 \div 5$ **8** $43\,414 \div 7$

*9 (a) $62 + 503 + 9$
    (b) $612 + 15 + 309 + 8$
    (c) $4016 + 213 + 8 + 20$
    (d) $615 + 29 + 306 + 1$
    (e) $1001 + 998 + 900 + 6$

*10 (a) $\begin{array}{r} 818 \\ -\ \underline{467} \end{array}$ (b) $\begin{array}{r} 306 \\ -\ \underline{152} \end{array}$ (c) $\begin{array}{r} 362 \\ -\ \underline{156} \end{array}$ (d) $\begin{array}{r} 478 \\ -\ \underline{169} \end{array}$

    (e) $\begin{array}{r} 4090 \\ -\ \underline{3365} \end{array}$ (f) $\begin{array}{r} 3080 \\ -\ \underline{1472} \end{array}$ (g) $\begin{array}{r} 300 \\ -\ \underline{172} \end{array}$ (h) $\begin{array}{r} 500 \\ -\ \underline{403} \end{array}$

    (i) $\begin{array}{r} 701 \\ -\ \underline{305} \end{array}$ (j) $\begin{array}{r} 406 \\ -\ \underline{128} \end{array}$

*11 (a) 59×8 (b) 87×6 (c) 97×7 (d) 83×9 (e) 92×8

*12 (a) 426×10 (b) 426×20 (c) 426×30 (d) 562×30 (e) 868×90

*13 (a) 63×15 (b) 42×25 (c) 67×81 (d) 95×87 (e) 99×88

*14 (a) $6126 \div 2$ (b) $4280 \div 5$ (c) $6272 \div 4$ (d) $8012 \div 4$ (e) $6072 \div 8$
(f) $8072 \div 8$ (g) $63027 \div 9$ (h) $80136 \div 8$

15 (a) $4066 \div 19$ (b) $6232 \div 19$ (c) $9519 \div 19$ (d) $3876 \div 19$

16 Remind yourself of the rules for divisibility (see page 224).

Which of 2, 3, 5, 6 or 9 will divide into:
(a) 32 (b) 45 (c) 36 (d) 815 (e) 825 (f) 312 (g) 540 (h) 504
(i) 405?

17 Do not set out questions like 3100×200 as long multiplication, nor head for your calculator! Simply ignore the zeros, work out 31×2, then put the zeros back on, giving $3100 \times 200 = 620000$.

Find:
(a) 5600×200 (b) 4600×300 (c) 35000×200 (d) 4000×15000.

18 State just the final figure of the answer in the following.

Do not work out the rest of the answer.

(a) 165×8 (b) 78×9 (c) 312×8 (d) 125×125 (e) 476×88
(f) 319×7

19 Each of my 15 tomato plants needs one can of water a day.

(a) How many cans of water are needed to water all the plants each day?

(b) How many cans are needed in a week?

(c) One capful of fertilizer feeds three plants. How many capfuls are needed for all 15 plants?

(d) A small bottle of fertilizer holds 20 capfuls. How many plants will it feed?

(e) A large bottle of fertilizer holds 50 capfuls. How many days will it last if I feed my 15 plants once every day?

20 Zita has 3 different skirts and 4 different blouses. How many different choices can she make if she is going to wear a skirt and blouse?

21 Mardi has 48 biscuits which she wants to share equally between her eight friends.

(a) How many biscuits does she have to give to each friend?

(b) Two of her friends do not want any biscuits (too fattening). How many *more* biscuits will the other friends receive than Mardi thought they would at first?

22 Figure 14:1 shows the number of boys and girls in a school in September for the five years from 1972 to 1976.

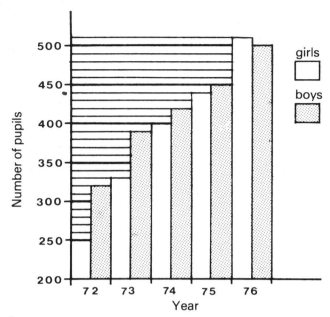

Fig. 14:1

(a) In which years were there more boys than girls?

(b) How many boys were there in 1974?

(c) How many girls were there in 1976?

(d) How many more girls were there in 1975 than in 1972?

(e) Which has increased most between 1972 and 1976, the number of boys or the number of girls?

23 Mr Kenner buys for the fifty teachers in the Charity Pools Club one £5 ticket a fortnight.

(a) How many tickets does he buy in a school year of 40 weeks?

(b) How much will the tickets cost altogether?

(c) How much must Mr Kenner collect from each teacher each week?

(d) If the teachers win a £75000 prize, how much will each receive if they share it equally?

24 Figure 14:2 shows two gear wheels. Wheel A has 8 teeth and wheel B has 16 teeth.

(a) How many turns of A before the timing marks come together again?

(b) When wheel A has turned 20 times how many times has wheel B turned?

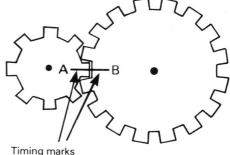

Timing marks

Fig. 14:2

25 Suppose the wheels in Figure 14:2 had 8 teeth and 12 teeth.

(a) How many turns of the small one would bring the timing marks together again?

(b) How many turns would the big wheel have then made?

(c) Simplify 8:12 by dividing each number by 4.

(d) How does your answer to part (c) tell you the answers to parts (a) and (b)?

26 Suppose the wheels in Figure 14:2 had 45 teeth and 63 teeth.

(a) Write 45:63 as simply as possible.

(b) How many turns of each wheel before the timing marks come together again?

27 To add a lot of marks in your head it is best to add the tens first.

Example   16 + 22 + 18 + 33 + 36 + 25 + 42
Add the tens (10 ... 30 ... 40 ... 70 ... 100 ... 120 ... 160).
Now add the units (166 ... 168 ... 176 ... 179 ... 185 ... 190 ... 192).
The answer is 192.

(a) 27 + 33 + 38 + 17 + 16 + 21 + 19

(b) 18 + 32 + 14 + 7 + 46 + 12 + 23 + 52

(c) Make up five more sets of marks (at least eight in each set). Add them up. Can you beat a calculator?

28 Aziz's calculator works perfectly except for the 0 key, which does not work at all. Investigate how Aziz can continue to use his calculator.

29 If you had to lose one of the four function keys on your calculator ($+$, $-$, $\times$, $\div$) which one would you choose and why?

15 Algebra: negative integer substitution

Substitution of negative numbers is often needed in physics.

For example, the formula for the distance travelled in t seconds by an object starting with a speed of u m/s and accelerating at a m/s^2 is $s = ut + \frac{1}{2}at^2$.

If the object is slowing down, then a will be negative.

Example If the ball in Figure 15:1 is thrown up at 8 m/s, its height after 1 second is found by substituting $u = 8$, $t = 1$ and $a = -9.81$ into the formula $s = ut + \frac{1}{2}at^2$.

Then $s = (8 \times 1) + (\frac{1}{2} \times -9.81 \times 1)$
$= 8 - 4.9$
$= 3.1$ m

Fig. 15:1

In questions 1, 2 and 3 substitute the values $x = 2$ and $y = 3$.

1 (a) $4x$ (b) $x + y$ (c) $2x + y$ (d) $x + 3y$ (e) $y - x$ (f) $3x - 2y$

2 (a) x^2 (b) $2y^2$ (c) $2x^2$ (d) $3x^2$ (e) x^3 (f) y^3

3 (a) xy (b) $2xy$ (c) x^2y (d) xy^2 (e) $10x^2y$ (f) $10x^2y^2$

In questions 4 to 7 substitute the values $x = -2$ and $y = -3$.

4 (a) $2x$ (b) $x + y$ (c) $x - y$ (d) $y - x$ (e) $7 - x$

5 (a) $x + 1$ (b) $x - 1$ (c) $y + 1$ (d) $y - 1$ (e) $1 - 3x$

6 (a) $3x - 1$ (b) $3y + 1$ (c) $3y - 1$ (d) $-2 + x$ (e) $-1 - x$

7 (a) x^2 (b) $2y^2$ (c) $2x^2$ (d) $3y^2$ (e) xy (f) $-xy$

*8 Substitute the values $x = -3$ and $y = -4$ into the expressions of question 6.

*9 Substitute the values $x = -3$ and $y = -4$ into the expressions of question 7.

10 Substitute the values $x = -2$ and $y = -3$ into:

    (a) $2x + y$ (b) $2x - y$ (c) $3x + 2y$ (d) $2y - 3x$ (e) $-2y - 3x$.

In questions 11 to 13 substitute the values $s = -1$, $t = -2$ and $u = 3$.

11 (a) $2t^2$ (b) $3st$ (c) $-2st$ (d) st^2 (e) s^2t (f) stu

12 (a) s^3 (b) $2t^3$ (c) $2s^2 + t^2$ (d) $2s^2 - t^2$ (e) $3s^2 + 2ut$ (f) $3s^2 - 2ut$

13 (a) $\dfrac{t}{s}$ (b) $\dfrac{s}{t}$ (c) $\dfrac{s}{u}$ (d) $\dfrac{2u}{t}$ (e) $\dfrac{6t}{u}$ (f) $\dfrac{3s}{2t}$

14

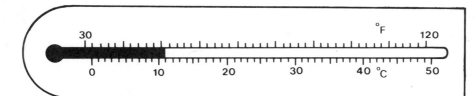

Fig. 15:2

The formula to change a temperature in °C into °F is $F = \dfrac{9C}{5} + 32$.

Change into °F:

(a) 5°C   (b) 0°C   (c) 100°C   (d) −5°C

(e) −10°C   (f) −15°C   (g) −3°C   (h) −4°C

(i) −40°C   (j) −273°C (the coldest possible, called 'absolute zero').

15 Draw a graph of $y = x^2$ taking values of x from −5 to 5.

16 Draw a graph of $y = x^3$ taking the values of x from −3 to +3 at 0.5 intervals.

16 Probability: one event

A   The probability scale

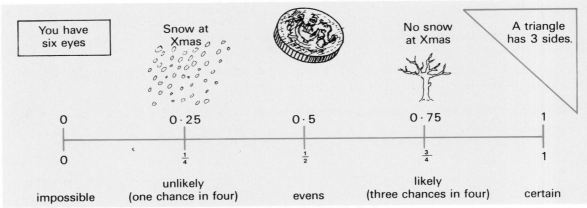

Fig. 16:1

1 Choose the probability 0, 0.5 or 1 for the following events.

(a) A man living for 250 years.   (b) A square having four sides.

(c) A tossed coin coming down heads.   (d) A hexagon having eight sides.

(e) A triangle having less than five sides.   (f) Next year being 1983.

(g) The person reading this being alive yesterday.

(h) The top card of a shuffled pack being a spade or a club.

2 Describe the following events as one of the following:
impossible; very unlikely; quite unlikely; evens; quite likely; very likely; certain.

(a) You are dealt thirteen cards of the same suit in a game of cards.

(b) Your teacher was born in a month with an 'r' in it.

(c) Next year will have Christmas Day on the 25th December.

(d) The next man to enter your classroom will be walking on his hands.

(e) The author was born on April 31st 1941.

(f) The next person who speaks to you will speak English.

(g) There is an odd number of lettuce seeds in a large packet.

3 Make up seven events of your own, one for each kind of chance given at the start of question 2 and in the same order.

4 Write about some examples of probability in life, trying to explain in what way they are used.

B   Probability calculations

Computers can produce random numbers. These are used when writing a program where you want chance to play a part, e.g. in games or quizzes.

RAND (or RANDOMIZE) starts the computer at a random place in its list of random numbers, which are all between 0 and 1.

INT takes the number before the decimal point, so if RND = 0.7 then RND*7 = 4.9 and INT(RND*7) = 4.

The following three programs illustrate random number production. In each case line 20 will give a random number between 0 and 6.

```
5 REM "SINCLAIR"      5 REM "380Z"           5 REM "BBC"
10 RAND              10 RANDOMIZE           20 PRINT
20 PRINT INT(RND*7)  20 PRINT INT(RND(1)*7)    INT(RND(1)*7)
```

The following two programs use the RND function to simulate chance events.

```
  5 REM "Simtoss"                Note
 10 PRINT "Simulated coin toss"  BBC computer needs
 20 RAND   (RANDOMIZE or omit)   6 PRINT CHR$(14)
 30 PRINT "How many tosses?"     to switch on paging.
 40 INPUT N
 50 LET H = 0
 60 LET T = 0                      5 REM "Simcard"
 70 FOR M = 1 TO N                10 RAND   (RANDOMIZE or omit)
 80 LET R = INT(RND*2)            20 LET M = INT(RND*4) + 1
    (You may need RND(1)*2)       30 LET N = INT(RND*13) + 1
 90 IF R = 1 THEN GOTO 130        40 LET N$ = STR$(N)
100 PRINT "TAILS"                 50 IF N = 1 THEN LET N$ = "A"
110 LET T = T + 1                 60 IF N = 11 THEN LET N$ = "J"
120 GOTO 150                      70 IF N = 12 THEN LET N$ = "Q"
130 PRINT "HEADS"                 80 IF N = 13 THEN LET N$ = "K"
140 LET H = H + 1                 90 IF LEN(N$) = 1 THEN LET N$ = "ᴧ" + N$
150 CLS   (Clear screen)         100 LET X$ = "SPADES"
160 NEXT M                       110 IF M = 1 THEN LET X$ = "CLUBS"
170 PRINT N; "ᴧ tosses."         120 IF M = 2 THEN LET X$ = "DIAMONDS"
180 PRINT H; "ᴧ heads; ᴧ ᴧ";     130 IF M = 3 THEN LET X$ = "HEARTS"
    T;"ᴧ tails."                  140 PRINT N$;"ᴧ of ᴧ";X$
                                 150 GOTO 20
```

1 Example   The chance of picking an ace from a pack is $\frac{4}{52} = \frac{1}{13}$.

State the probability of the following events as a fraction, simplified if possible.

(a) Picking the ace of clubs from a pack of cards.

(b) Picking a black card from a pack of cards.

(c) Dying on a Sunday.

(d) Buying the winning ticket in a raffle if you buy one and 100 are sold.

(e) Throwing a six with one throw of a die. ('Dice' is for more than one die.)

*2   State the chance of the following.

(a) Picking a heart-card from a pack.

(b) Picking a king from a pack.

(c) Picking the King of Hearts from a pack.

(d) Scoring 1 with one throw of a die.

(e) An unborn baby being a boy.

(f) Scoring an even number with one throw of a die.

(g) A number, picked at random from 5, 6, 7, 8, 9, 10, 11, 12 being a square number.

(h) Picking a red ball from a bag of 1 red and 5 green balls.

(i) Picking the green ball from the bag in part (h).

3 Learn:

The probability of an event happening is $\dfrac{\text{The number of ways it could happen}}{\text{The total possible number of events}}$ if all outcomes are equally likely.

Example   To find the probability of scoring an even number (2, 4 or 6) on a die.

The number of ways it could happen is 3.

The total possible number of events is 6.

The probability of the event is $\frac{3}{6} = \frac{1}{2}$.

State the probability of:

(a) being dealt a heart *or* a club from a pack of cards

(b) being dealt an ace *or* a king from a pack or cards.

4

● ● ● ○ ● ○ ○ ○

Fig. 16:2

The eight coloured balls in Figure 16:2 are put into a bag.

The chance of picking a black ball is $\frac{4}{8} = \frac{1}{2}$.

What is the chance of picking (each time from the full bag):
(a) an orange ball   (b) a white ball   (c) a purple ball?

5 A bag contains 6 red, 5 blue, 3 white and 2 green balls.

What is the chance of picking (each time from the full bag):
(a) a white   (b) a red   (c) a blue   (d) a green   (e) a black?

6 Two balls are taken from the bag in question 5, one after the other.

If the first ball is red, what is the chance that the second ball is:
(a) red   (b) blue   (c) white   (d) green?

7 Repeat question 6 if the first ball is:
(i) blue   (ii) white.

8 Add together the answer fractions for the five answers to question 5. Do the same for the four answers to question 6. Give a reason for the answers you obtain.

9 Two dice are thrown and the scores are added. Copy and complete the table, which shows all the possible totals in all the possible ways.

Score on 1st die

Add	1	2	3	4	5	6
Score 1	2	3				
on 2		4	5			
2nd 3	4		6			
die 4						
5						
6						

10 Use your table for question 9 to state the probability that the total score from a throw of two dice will be:
   (a) 6   (b) 3   (c) 5   (d) 10   (e) 1   (f) 2   (g) 7   (h) 9.

11 A coin is tossed four times. The 'tree diagram' in Figure 16:3 shows all the possible results and the probability of each result. Copy and complete Figure 16:3.

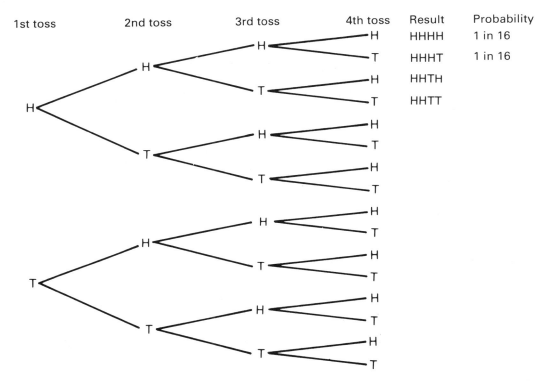

Fig. 16:3

12 Use the tree diagram drawn in question 11 to find the probability of getting, in any order:
   (a) 2 heads and 2 tails
   (b) 3 heads and 1 tail
   (c) 4 heads
   (d) 1 head and 3 tails
   (e) no heads.

13 By experiment compare theoretical probability with actual events. The events in questions 9 and 11 would be possible ones to use.

   Write about your findings and be prepared to discuss them with your class.

For Discussion

Figure 17:1 shows the dial on a spring balance.

What weight is on the balance when the pointer is at each of the marked letters?

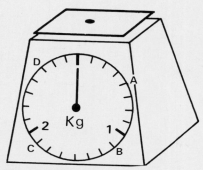

Fig. 17:1

1 Add 17.61 to 5.3

2 Find the sum of 14, 0.42, 4 and 40.

3 Find the difference between: (a) 168 and 9169   (b) 1.68 and 91.69

4 Which is bigger, and by how much: (a) 4.6 or 4.7   (b) 3.15 or 3.09?

5 Write as a decimal fraction: (a) 1 tenth   (b) 1 hundredth.

6 (a) State the value of the figure 1 in 0.010

(b) Write 10 hundredths as a decimal fraction.

7 Copy Figure 17:2 accurately. Write on your copy the number for each arrow.

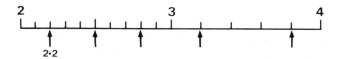

Fig. 17:2

8 Copy the following pairs of number bonds, then write = or ≠ between them.

(a) $6 + 2$ $2 + 6$ (b) $6 - 2$ $2 - 6$ (c) 4×3 3×4 (d) $10 \div 2$ $2 \div 10$

9 Give answers to the following, or say if they are impossible.

(a) $3 - 4$ (b) 2.4×2 (c) $6 \div 3$ (d) $3 \div 6$

10 What is 69 times 24?

11 Use the answer to question 10 to find:

(a) 6.9×24 (b) 6.9×2.4 (c) 0.69×2.4 (d) 0.69×0.24

12 (a) $6.8 \div 2$ (b) $3.12 \div 3$ (c) $4.8 \div 12$

13 (a) $6.8 \div 0.2$ (b) $3.12 \div 0.3$ (c) $4.8 \div 1.2$

*14 Figure 17:3 shows three questions that Jill got wrong.

Write out the correct answers, and try to explain briefly what Jill did wrong in each one.

(a) $1.8 + 2 + 20$?   (b) $7.6 - 3$?   (c) $4.8 - 2.9$?

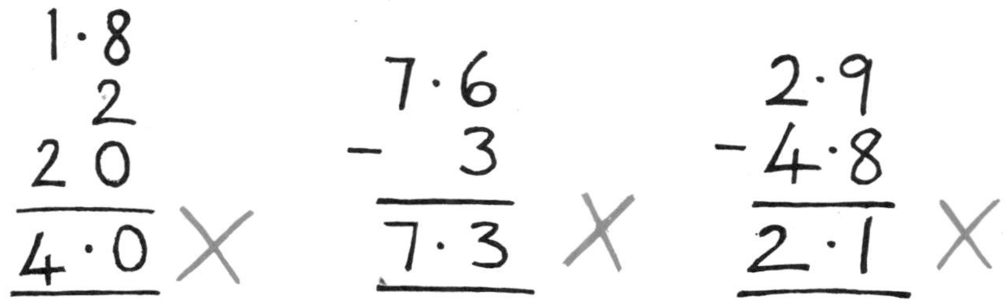

$$
\begin{array}{r}
1.8 \\
2 \\
20 \\
\hline
4.0 \\
\end{array} \times
\qquad
\begin{array}{r}
7.6 \\
- 3 \\
\hline
7.3 \\
\end{array} \times
\qquad
\begin{array}{r}
2.9 \\
- 4.8 \\
\hline
2.1 \\
\end{array} \times
$$

Fig. 17:3

*15 Find the sum of:

(a) 6, 17 and 3.4   (b) 3.9, 50 and 7.5   (c) 4.8, 57 and 6.41
(d) 3.65, 70, 1.8 and 5.

*16 (a) Take 11.6 from 23.8

(b) Take 13.5 from 35.3

(c) Find the difference between 4.96 and 1.99

(d) Find the difference between 6.12 and 18.83

*17 Rewrite the numbers in question 15 when each is made one tenth (0.1) bigger.
Start (a) 6.1, 17.1 and . . .

*18 Take 1 hundredth from:
(a) 0.08   (b) 6.07   (c) 3.19   (d) 5.81   (e) 5.80

*19 Use the answer to part (a) to write the answers to the rest of the question.
(a) 45×13 (b) 45×1.3 (c) 4.5×13 (d) 4.5×1.3 (e) 0.45×13
(f) 0.45×1.3 (g) 0.45×0.13

*20 (a) $7.8 \div 2$ (b) $1.41 \div 3$ (c) $8.72 \div 8$ (d) $16.012 \div 4$

*21 (a) $5.6 \div 0.2$ (b) $56 \div 0.2$ (c) $8.4 \div 0.4$ (d) $84 \div 0.4$ (e) $0.84 \div 4$
(f) $0.84 \div 0.4$ (g) $1.76 \div 0.2$ (h) $3.55 \div 0.5$

22 (a) Find the difference between 17 and 0.64

(b) Take 1.57 from 9.

(c) Take 2.08 from 13.

23 (a) $16.11 \div 0.09$ (b) $0.105 \div 0.7$ (c) $6 \div 0.3$ (d) $0.3 \div 6$

24 (a) 3.95 add 1 tenth   (b) 3.95 add 1 hundredth   (c) 3.95 add 5 hundredths
(d) 3.95 take 1 tenth   (e) 4 take 1 tenth   (f) 4 take 1 hundredth

25 (a) 6.19×10 (b) 7.35×100 (c) 6.3×100 (d) $7 \div 10$ (e) $7.9 \div 10$
(f) $7.62 \div 10$ (g) $0.36 \div 10$ (h) $16.8 \div 100$ (i) $1.68 \div 100$

26 Change to a decimal fraction:
(a) $\frac{1}{4}$ (b) $\frac{1}{8}$ (c) $\frac{3}{8}$ (d) $\frac{2}{5}$ (e) $\frac{1}{16}$.

27 In 1983 a factory employed 1000 machine-operators, 100 drivers and 10 night-watchmen. Each worked 8 hours a day for 5 days a week. A machine-operator earned £3.28 an hour, a driver earned £3.62 an hour and a night-watchman earned £2.93 an hour.

(a) How much did each kind of workman earn in a day?

(b) How much did it cost the factory each day for:
(i) its machine-operators   (ii) its drivers   (iii) its night-watchmen?

(c) What is the total wages bill for the five-day week?

28 My old ruler is not marked in cm, only in inches and tenths of inches. I know that 1 inch is 2.54 cm.

(a) How many cm is 3 inches?

(b) How many cm is $3\frac{6}{10}$ inches?

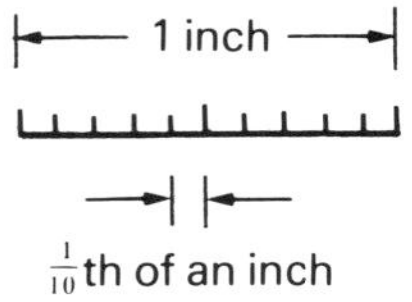

Fig. 17:4 $\frac{1}{10}$ th of an inch

29 Taking a rough approximation of 2.5 cm to an inch, how many inches is:
(a) 10 cm   (b) 7 cm   (c) 1 cm?

30 Let's devise a metric day!

We'll divide each day into 10 decidays (d-days or dd), and each deciday into 100 millidays (md).

(a) How many minutes in a day?   (b) How many millidays in a day?

(c) How many minutes is one milliday?   (d) How many hours is 1 dd?

(e) 1 hour $= \frac{1}{2.4} = \frac{10}{24} = \frac{5}{12}$ decidays; so 3 hours $= \frac{15}{12} = 1.25$ dd.

How many dd is:
(i) 6 hours   (ii) 9 hours   (iii) 12 hours   (iv) 4 hours   (v) 8 hours?

(f) Design a deciday clock and show on it the 24-hour clock time:
(i) 0300   (ii) 0900   (iii) 1200   (iv) 1600.

(g) After the French Revolution, the government tried to metricate time. Find out more about this effort (which failed!).

Using your calculator

Somerset County Council

SOMERSET COUNTY COUNCIL
1983
MAIN SERVICE STATISTICS

Education

	Pupils	Teachers	Schools
Primary	31 798	1335	239
Secondary	32 548	1859	40
Special	1138	116	8
Further Education	5850	746	6

Social Services	Nos.
Elderly aged 65 and over	73800
Children in care	530
Registered physically handicapped	6926
Day centres for the disabled – clients	749
Elderly persons' homes – places provided	1062
Home-help hours	728800
Meals-on-wheels served	184000
Highways	
Length of roads maintained	km
– principal	632
– non-principal	5821
Fire Brigade	
Number of calls answered	4058
Libraries	
Number of libraries (including 9 mobile)	43
Number of books issued each year	5400000

Use the information in the above table, and your calculator, to answer the following questions.

1 Altogether, how many:
(a) pupils   (b) teachers   (c) schools?

2 On average, to the nearest whole number, how many pupils per teacher in:
(a) primary schools   (b) secondary schools   (c) special schools
(d) colleges of further education?

3 Which is the greater, and by how much:
(a) the number of pupils   (b) the number of elderly people?

4 The council spent £98800000 on education in 1983. How much is this, on average:
(a) per school   (b) per pupil?

5 The Fire Service cost £3900000 to run. What was the average cost of calling out the fire brigade?

6 The population of the county in 1983 was 405000. How many library books were borrowed per person that year on average?

7 There were 835 employees connected with the Highways Department. How many kilometres of road per employee, to the nearest 0.5 km?

A Experimental dissections

Experiment 1

Fig. 18:1

Experiment 2

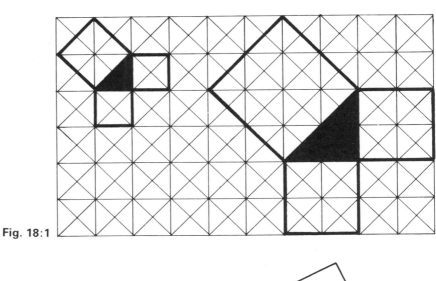

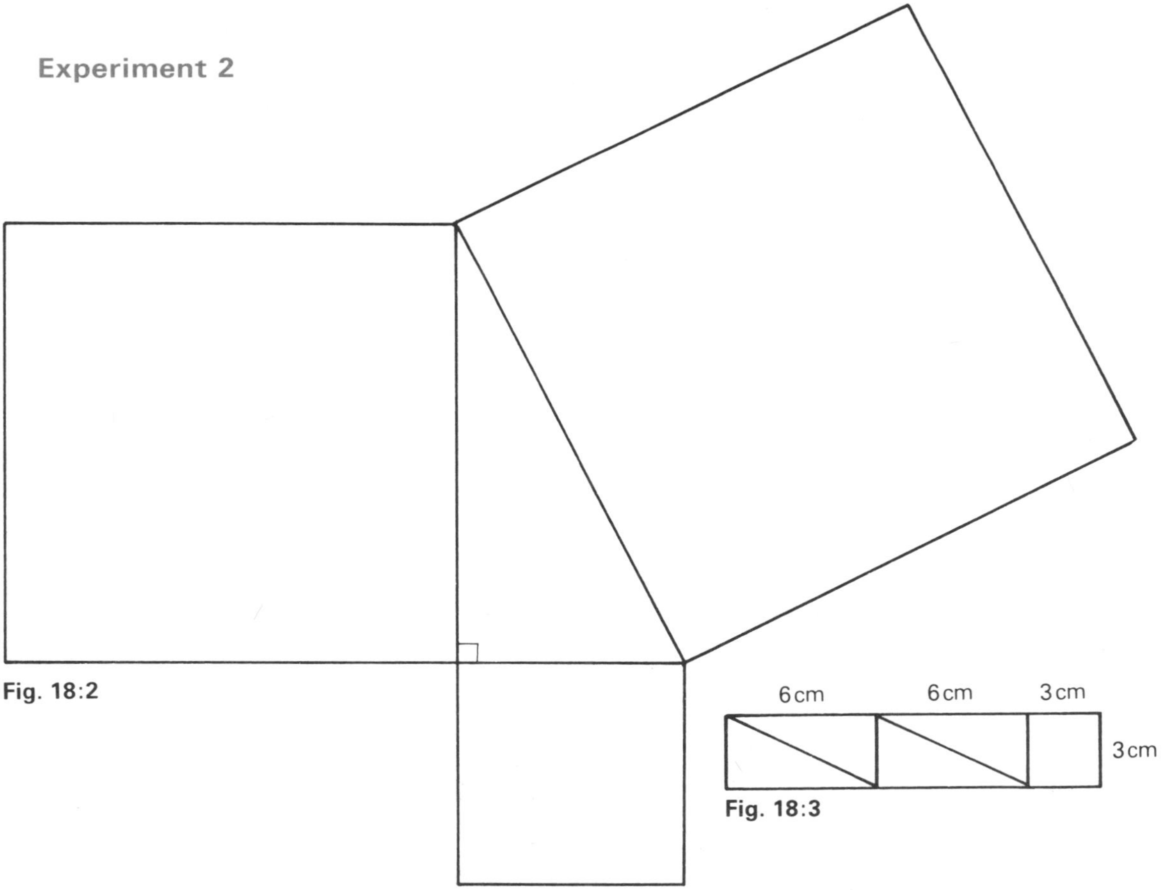

Fig. 18:2

Fig. 18:3

6 cm 6 cm 3 cm

3 cm

Experiment 3

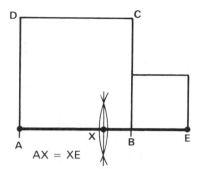

AX = XE

Fig. 18:4

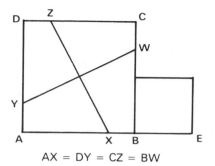

AX = DY = CZ = BW

Fig. 18:5

Experiment 4

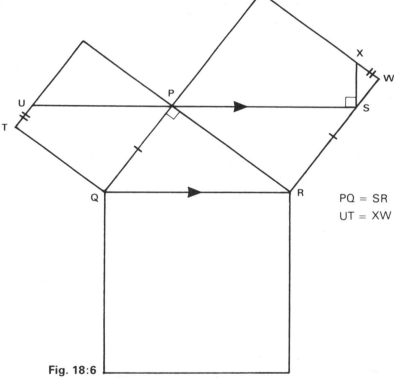

PQ = SR
UT = XW

Fig. 18:6

Experiment 5

Fig. 18:7

B Counting squares

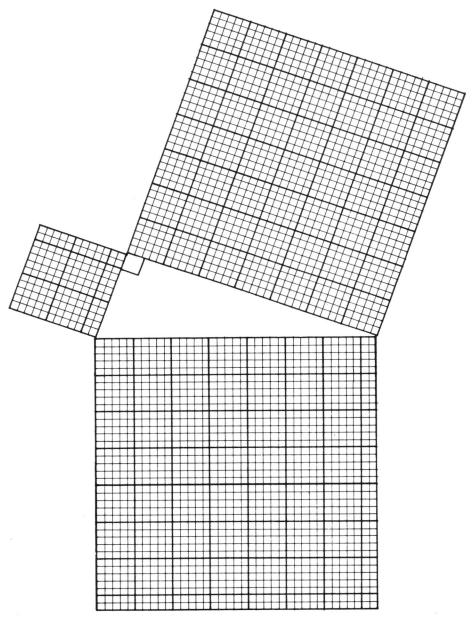

Fig. 18:8

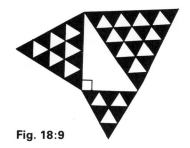

Fig. 18:9

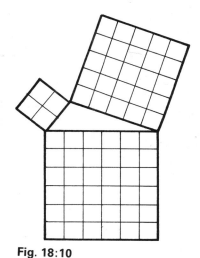

Fig. 18:10

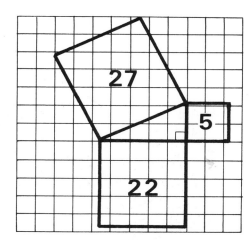

Fig. 18:11

C Pythagoras' Theorem

'The square on the hypotenuse of a right-angled triangle is equal to the sum of the squares on the other two sides'

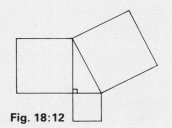

Fig. 18:12

1 The square in Figure 18:13 is drawn on a 3 cm line. It has an area of 3 cm × 3 cm = 9 cm².

State the area of the square drawn on a line of length:
(a) 5 cm   (b) 6 cm   (c) 7 cm   (d) 8 cm
(e) 9 cm   (f) 10 cm.

Fig. 18:13

2 The **square** of a number is the number multiplied by itself.

At least one of the following sequences of key presses will give you the square of 7 (49) on a calculator. Find which ones work on your calculator.

7 $\boxed{\times}$ 7 $\boxed{=}$ 7 $\boxed{\times}$ $\boxed{=}$ 7 $\boxed{\times}$ $\boxed{\times}$ $\boxed{=}$

7 $\boxed{\times}$ $\boxed{k}$ $\boxed{=}$ 7 $\boxed{x^2}$

Using your calculator, or long multiplication, copy and complete this table for squares.

Side in cm	11	12	13	14	15	16	17	18	19	20
Area in cm^2	121	144	169							

3 The **hypotenuse** of a right-angled triangle is the longest side. It is always opposite the right angle. We have found that **the area of the square on the hypotenuse is equal to the sum of the squares on the other two sides**. This is **Pythagoras' Theorem**; Pythagoras was an Ancient Greek mathematician. He is credited with being the first person to prove that this theorem is true for all right-angled triangles.

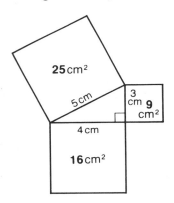

Fig. 18:14

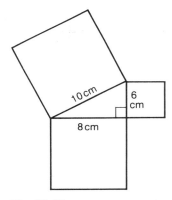

Fig. 18:15

In Figure 18:14,

Area of square on hypotenuse = 25 cm^2
Area of square on 3 cm side   = 9 cm^2 25 = 9 + 16
Area of square on 4 cm side   = 16 cm^2

Copy Figure 18:15. It need not be drawn very accurately nor the correct size.

Now copy and complete:

For a right-angled triangle, sides 10 cm, 8 cm and 6 cm:

Area of square on hypotenuse = . . . cm^2
Area of square on 8 cm side   = . . . cm^2 . . . = . . . + . . .
Area of square on . . . . = . . . cm^2

4 Copy Figure 18:16, about the same size as drawn, then copy and complete:

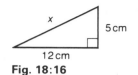

Fig. 18:16

Area of square on 5 cm side = . . .
Area of square on 12 cm side = . . .
So the area of the square on the hypotenuse must be . . . cm^2.
x must therefore be . . . cm (using the table in question 2).

*5 Using the table for question 2, or a calculator, state the area of each square in Figure 18:17.

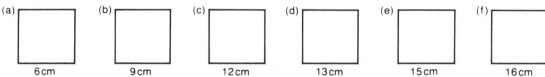

Fig. 18:17

*6 Using the table for question 2, or a calculator, state the length of the side of each square in Figure 18:18.

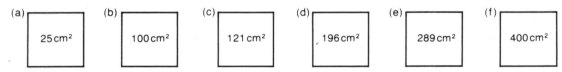

Fig. 18:18

*7 Copy and complete this table, continuing the one for question 2.

x	21	22	23	24	25	26	27	28	29	30
x^2	441									

*8 In the table for question 7, if x is the side of a square then x^2 is its area.

If a square has an area of 729 cm^2, how long is its side?

*9 Copy Figure 18:19, about the same size, then copy and complete the table.

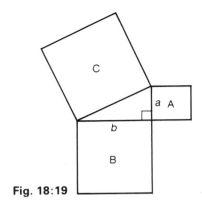

Fig. 18:19

Length a	3 cm	4 cm	2 cm	3 cm	6 cm	8 cm	10 cm	7 cm	11 cm
Length b	5 cm	7 cm	3 cm	6 cm	7 cm	9 cm	4 cm	8 cm	5 cm
Area A	9 cm^2	16 cm^2							
Area B	25 cm^2	49 cm^2							
Area C	34 cm^2								

10 Referring to Figure 18:19, state the values of (a) to (g) in the following table. Do not copy the table.

Area of C	(a)	(b)	11 cm^2	13 cm^2	(e)	14 cm^2	38 cm^2
Area of A	4 cm^2	5 cm^2	(c)	4 cm^2	11 cm^2	(f)	19 cm^2
Area of B	6 cm^2	3 cm^2	5 cm^2	(d)	16 cm^2	12 cm^2	(g)

11 Copy and complete this table.

x	10	20	30	40	50	60
x^2						

12 Copy Figure 18:20, then copy and complete:

Area of square on hypotenuse = 37×37 cm^2 = ... cm^2
Area of square on 35 cm side = ... cm^2 = ... cm^2
So area of square on third side must be   ... cm^2
Therefore x must be ... cm

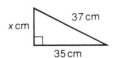

Fig. 18:20

13 For each triangle in Figure 18:21 find the areas of the squares on the given sides, then work out the area of the square on the third side and hence find the length marked x cm. Be very careful as to whether you should add or subtract the two known squares.

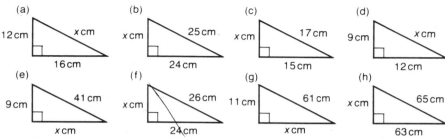

Fig. 18:21

14 In Figure 18:22 the squares on the three sides will have areas of h^2 cm^2, a^2 cm^2, and b^2 cm^2.

As the triangle is right-angled, we know that $h^2 = a^2 + b^2$.

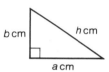

Fig. 18:22

Example   Calculate x in Figure 18:23.

$h = x$ cm; $a = 5$ cm; $b = 3$ cm

$h^2 = a^2 + b^2 \rightarrow x^2 = 5^2 + 3^2 = 25 + 9 = 34$

As $x^2 = 34$ then x is not a whole number. It must be a little less than 6 (as $6^2 = 36$).

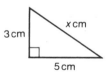

Fig. 18:23

If your calculator has a $\boxed{\sqrt{}}$ key you can use it to find x very accurately (though not exactly as there is no exact number that squares to make 34).

For the triangles in Figure 18:24 find the value of x to the nearest whole number.

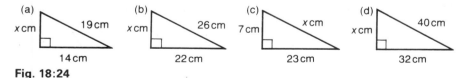

Fig. 18:24

15 Draw some large charts showing the dissections of exercise 18A.

16 Find out more about the Pythagoreans from a mathematical encyclopaedia.

19 Ratios; proportional division

A Ratio, 1:*x*

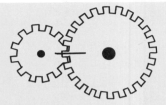

These gear wheels give a gear ratio of 1:2.

The large wheel has 24 teeth and the smaller wheel has 12 teeth, so the larger wheel turning once makes the smaller wheel turn twice.

Fig. 19:1

Ratios can be written using the word 'to', using a colon (:), or as a fraction.

Example   12 to 24 = 1 to 2 = 1:2 = $\frac{1}{2}$

1   The ratio of John's money to Carol's money is 1:2. What is the ratio of Carol's money to John's?

2   Dad is 2 metres tall; Sam is 1 metre tall. What is the ratio of:
   (a) Dad's height to Sam's height   (b) Sam's height to Dad's height?

3   Write the ratio 1 to 3 as a fraction.

4
   Fig. 19:2

   CD is twice as long as AB, so CD:AB = 2:1 and AB:CD = 1:2.

   EF is three times as long as AB, so EF:AB = 3:1 and AB:EF = 1:3.

   Copy Figure 19:2, then write a sentence like the ones above about GH and AB

5   In this question the lines AB, CD, EF and GH are in the same ratio as they were in Figure 19:2, but they are not the lengths drawn there.

   (a) If AB is 5 cm long, how long is: (i) CD   (ii) EF   (iii) GH?

   (b) If CD is 8 cm long, how long is: (i) AB   (ii) EF   (iii) GH?

   (c) If EF is 6 cm long, how long is: (i) AB   (ii) CD   (iii) GH?

6   The ratio of the distance Jane cycles to the distance Jill cycles is 3:1.

   (a) How many times as far as Jill goes does Jane go?

   (b) If Jill goes 3 km, how far does Jane go?

7 The ratio of the top speed of my moped to that of Franco's car is 1:3. My moped's top speed is 70 km/h. What is the top speed of Franco's car?

8 Mo's tail : Minnie's tail = 1 : 4. Minnie's tail is 8 cm long. How long is Mo's?

*9 Copy the lines in Figure 19:3, then write the following as a ratio of two numbers. **Example** MN : IJ = 5 : 1

(a) IJ : KL   (b) KL : IJ   (c) IJ : MN   (d) PQ : IJ   (e) IJ : PQ

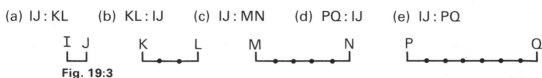

Fig. 19:3

*10 In this question the lines IJ, KL, MN and PQ are in the same ratio as they were in Figure 19:3, but they are not the lengths drawn there.

(a) If IJ is 6 cm long, how long is: (i) KL   (ii) MN   (iii) PQ?

(b) If KL is 9 cm long, how long is: (i) IJ   (ii) MN   (iii) PQ?

(c) If MN is 10 cm long, how long is: (i) IJ   (ii) KL   (iii) PQ?

(d) If PQ is 7 cm long, how long is: (i) IJ   (ii) KL   (iii) MN?

*11 The ratio of Jeff's weight to Abe's is 1 : 2. Abe weighs 50 kg. What does Jeff weigh?

12 If AB is twice as long as CD you can either write
AB : CD = 2 : 1 or CD : AB = 1 : 2.

Write two statements each if:
(a) EF is 3 times as long as GH   (b) IJ is 4 times as long as KL.

13 Copy Figure 19:4 exactly, then mark a point C on the line so that AB : BC = 1 : 3. Write on your line the length of BC.

A   2cm   B

Fig. 19:4

14 In Figure 19:5, QR is twice as long as PQ, so QR : PQ = 2 : 1.

Write a similar statement about:
(a) RS and PQ (Start your answer 'RS is 3 times as long ...')
(b) ST and RS   (c) ST and QR   (d) ST and PQ.

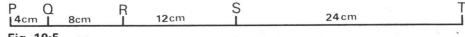

Fig. 19:5

95

15 In Figure 19:5, PQ is $\frac{1}{2}$ of QR, and PQ is $\frac{1}{3}$ of RS.

What fraction is: (a) QR of ST   (b) RS of ST   (c) PQ of ST?

---

16 Draw Figure 19:6 on squared paper. Then draw a larger rectangle, the same shape but with sides in the ratio 2:1 to the first.

Fig. 19:6

17 The smaller rectangle you drew has 8 squares. How many squares has the larger? What is the ratio of the number of squares in the smaller to the number in the larger?

18 Copy Figure 19:7 on squared paper. Draw larger shapes with sides in the ratio 2:1 with the first. Each time find the ratio of the number of squares in the smaller to the number in the larger.

Fig. 19:7

19 Repeat question 18 with the larger shapes' sides in the ratio 3:1 to the smaller. What can you deduce about the ratio of the areas of similar shapes?

B   Simplifying ratios

A		B		C		D
	3 cm		5 cm		7 cm	

Fig. 19:8

AB = 3 cm and BC = 5 cm, so the ratio AB : BC = 3 : 5.

AB = 3 cm and BD = 12 cm, so the ratio AB : BD = 3 : 12.

The ratio 3:12 can be simplified by dividing both numbers by 3, giving AB : BD = 1 : 4.

1 Simplify to the smallest possible numbers:
(a) 20 : 30 (divide both by 10)   (b) 28:35 (divide both by 7)
(c) 15 : 20   (d) 16 : 24   (e) 30 : 12   (f) 40 : 24.

*2 Simplify:
(a) 8 : 20 (÷ by 4)   (b) 12 : 28 (÷ by 4)   (c) 18 : 27 (÷ by 9)
(d) 48 : 40 (÷ by 8)   (e) 49 : 56 (÷ by 7)   (f) 63 : 49 (÷ by 7)
(g) 64 : 56 (÷ by 8)   (h) 36 : 63 (÷ by 9)   (i) 40 : 56 (÷ by 8).

*3 Simplify:
(a) 6 : 10   (b) 6 : 9   (c) 10 : 30   (d) 15 : 25.

4 Copy the following, replacing the stars by the correct numbers.
(a) 24 : 15 = 8 : *   (b) 15 : * = 5 : 3   (c) 20 : * = 5 : 7   (d) * : 18 = 11 : 9
(e) * : 9 = 7 : 3

5 Copy and complete:
(a) 8 : 12 : 16 = 2 : 3 : *   (b) 9 : 18 : 36 = 1 : * : *   (c) 12 : 15 : 27 = 4 : * : *

6 Fractions can be simplified like ratios. Simplify the following, making sure your final numbers are as small as possible. If necessary, divide more than once.

(a) $\dfrac{5}{15}$ (b) $\dfrac{9}{27}$ (c) $\dfrac{8}{24}$ (d) $\dfrac{10}{90}$ (e) $\dfrac{12}{16}$ (f) $\dfrac{10}{25}$ (g) $\dfrac{20}{36}$

(h) $\dfrac{22}{88}$ (i) $\dfrac{24}{84}$ (j) $\dfrac{45}{75}$ (k) $\dfrac{18}{48}$ (l) $\dfrac{33}{55}$ (m) $\dfrac{28}{98}$ (n) $\dfrac{30}{135}$

7 For the line shown in Figure 19:9 (which is not to scale): BC:AB = 3:1; CD : AB = 2 : 1;   DE : AB = 4 : 1.

What lengths should be written on:
(a) BC   (b) CD   (c) DE?

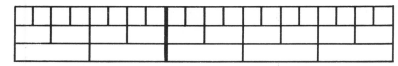

Fig. 19:9

8 Repeat question 7 if BC : AB = 2 : 1;   AB : CD = 1 : 3;   DE : BC = 1 : 2.

9 Repeat question 7 if DE : AB = 4 : 1;   CD : DE = 2 : 1;   BC : DE = 1 : 2.

10 Figure 19:10 illustrates that 8:12 = 4:6 = 2:3.

Fig. 19:10

Draw a similar diagram to illustrate 6 : 9 : 12 = 4 : 6 : 8 = 2 : 3 : 4.

C Using ratios

For Discussion

Example Ann's pay to Tom's pay is in the ratio 4 : 5. Ann earns £100. What does Tom earn?

Divide Ann's pay into the 4 parts of her ratio, giving £25 a part. Tom receives 5 of these parts, giving: *Answer* 5 × £25 = £125.

Fig. 19:11

Further questions

(a) Cement : sand = 2 : 7
6 kg cement. How much sand?
56 kg sand. How much cement?

(b) Girls to boys = 3 : 2
24 boys. How many girls?
30 girls. How many boys?

(c) Ratio kilometres to miles = 8 to 5
15 miles. How many kilometres?
40 kilometres. How many miles?

Fig. 19:12

1 Anne's height to Beryl's is in the ratio 3 : 4. If Anne is 90 cm tall, how tall is Beryl?

2 AB : CD = 3 : 5. If AB is 12 cm long:
(a) how long is each part of AB
(b) how long is CD?

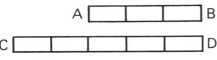

Fig. 19:14

Fig. 19:13

3 (a) How long is RS if PQ is: (i) 3 cm   (ii) 6 cm   (iii) 15 cm   (iv) 21 cm?

(b) How long is PQ if RS is: (i) 42 cm   (ii) 56 cm?

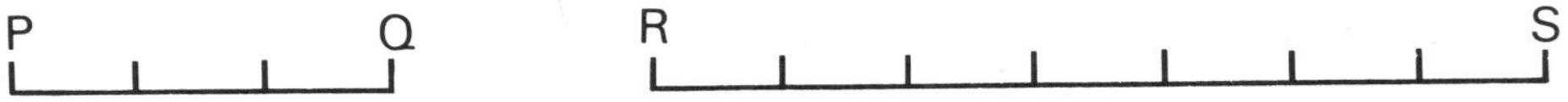

P   Q   R   S

Fig. 19:15

4 Copy Figure 19:16 exactly, then draw a line GH such that EF:GH = 2:3. Write the length of GH on it.

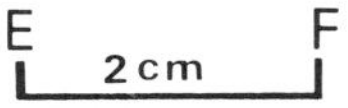

Fig. 19:16

5 Copy Figure 19:17 exactly, then divide it into two equal parts. Finally, draw a line KL such that IJ:KL = 2:3 and write the length of KL on it.

Fig. 19:17

6 Copy Figure 19:18 exactly, then draw a line OP such that MN:OP = 3:2. (Hint: Split MN into 3 parts.) Write the length of OP on it.

Fig. 19:18

7 Copy Figure 19:19 exactly, then draw a line ST such that QR:ST = 2:1, writing the length of ST on it.

Fig. 19:19

8 In Figure 19:20, calculate XY if VW = 10 cm and VW:XY = 2:3.

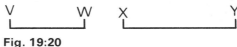

Fig. 19:20

*9 Figure 19:21 shows three sails neatly stowed away. Spar AB is divided into three equal parts by the sails.

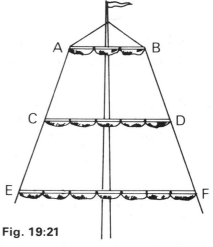

    (a) If spar AB is 6 metres long, how long is each part of it?

    (b) How many parts on spar CD?

    (c) How long is CD? (Hint: Use the answers to (a) and (b).)

    (d) How long is EF?

Questions 10 to 14 all refer to Figure 19:21.

Fig. 19:21

*10 If AB is 9 metres long, how long is: (a) each part of AB   (b) CD   (c) EF?

*11 If AB is 15 metres long, how long is: (a) CD   (b) EF?

*12 If CD is 5 metres long, how long is: (a) AB   (b) EF?

*13 If CD is 20 metres long, how long is: (a) AB   (b) EF?

*14 If EF is 49 feet long, how many feet long is: (a) AB   (b) CD?

*15 (a) In Figure 19:22, into how many parts has GH been divided?

(b) If GH = 9 cm, how long is each part?　　(c) If GH : IJ = 3 : 5, how long is IJ?

Fig. 19:22

*16 In Figure 19:22, find IJ if GH:IJ = 3:5 and:
(a) GH = 3 cm　　(b) GH = 12 cm　　(c) GH = 15 cm　　(d) GH = 6 cm.

17 Calculate the length of XY if:
(a) VW = 18 cm and VW : XY = 3 : 2　　(b) VW = 15 cm and VW : XY = 5 : 6.

18 Calculate the length of VW if:
(a) XY = 8 cm and VW : XY = 3 : 4　　(b) XY = 6 cm and VW : XY = 4 : 3.

Fig. 19:23　　A　　　　　　　　　　　B

19 A circus transports its animals in wagons, each holding the same number. Say wagon-train A carries 6 ponies.

(a) How many ponies in each wagon?
(b) How many ponies could wagon-train B carry?

20 If A carries 9 bears, how many bears can B carry?

21 If B carries 20 monkeys, how many monkeys can A carry?

22 If B carries 100 performing fleas, how many fleas can A carry?

23 Wagons A cost £1500 altogether. What did wagons B cost altogether?

24 Wagons B weigh $2\frac{1}{2}$ tonnes altogether, when empty. What do wagons A weigh altogether, when empty?

25 A recipe for Orange Jelly:

500 ml water　　150 g sugar　　80 g gelatine
6 oranges　　2 lemons　　[Serves 6]

Write out the recipe in the same ratio, but to serve:
(a) 12 people　　(b) 3 people　　(c) 9 people.

Fig. 19:24

26 A bicycle has 3 gears. The ratios of the distance travelled for one turn of the pedals in different gears are:
1st gear : 2nd gear = 1 : 2
1st gear : 3rd gear = 2 : 5

In 1st gear, one turn of the pedals moves the cycle 50 cm.

(a) How far will one turn of the pedals move the bicycle in:
    (i) 2nd gear   (ii) 3rd gear?

(b) How many turns of the pedals to go 1 km in:
    (i) 1st gear   (ii) 2nd gear   (iii) 3rd gear?

Fig. 19:25

---

27 In Figure 19:26, BD is parallel to CE. The ratio AB:BC is 2:1. Measure AD and DE in mm. Write the ratio AD:DE as simply as possible. Draw your own triangle ACE, then try other ratios to see if AB:BC always equals AD:DE.

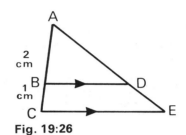

Fig. 19:26

28 A, B and C share some money. A has $\frac{1}{3}$ of it. B and C share the rest in the ratio 3 : 2 and C receives £30. How much money was there to start with?

D   Proportional division

For Discussion

Example   Divide £36 in the ratio 5 : 4.

    5 : 4 gives 9 parts.
    £36 divided into 9 parts gives £4 for each part.

      5 parts = £20   4 parts = £16
Fig. 19:27

Further question

Brass contains copper and zinc in the ratio 2 : 1.

How much copper and zinc is there in:
(a) 30 g of brass   (b) 45 g of brass   (c) 6 kg of brass?

1   In Figure 19:28, AX:XB = 2:5.

    If AB is 14 cm long, how long is: (a) AX   (b) XB?

    Fig. 19:28

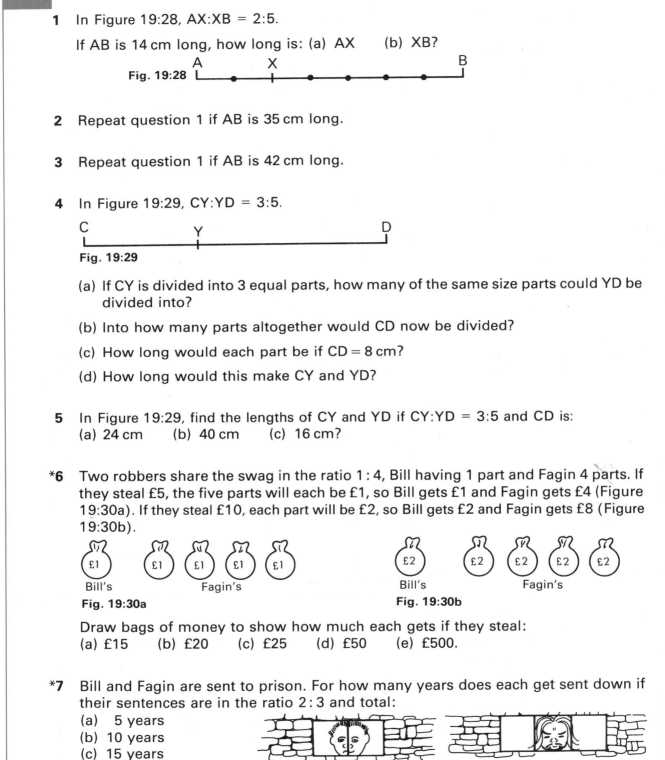

2   Repeat question 1 if AB is 35 cm long.

3   Repeat question 1 if AB is 42 cm long.

4   In Figure 19:29, CY:YD = 3:5.

    Fig. 19:29

    (a) If CY is divided into 3 equal parts, how many of the same size parts could YD be divided into?

    (b) Into how many parts altogether would CD now be divided?

    (c) How long would each part be if CD = 8 cm?

    (d) How long would this make CY and YD?

5   In Figure 19:29, find the lengths of CY and YD if CY:YD = 3:5 and CD is:
    (a) 24 cm   (b) 40 cm   (c) 16 cm?

*6 Two robbers share the swag in the ratio 1 : 4, Bill having 1 part and Fagin 4 parts. If they steal £5, the five parts will each be £1, so Bill gets £1 and Fagin gets £4 (Figure 19:30a). If they steal £10, each part will be £2, so Bill gets £2 and Fagin gets £8 (Figure 19:30b).

    £1   £1   £1   £1   £1

    Bill's   Fagin's
    Fig. 19:30a

    £2   £2   £2   £2   £2

    Bill's   Fagin's
    Fig. 19:30b

    Draw bags of money to show how much each gets if they steal:
    (a) £15   (b) £20   (c) £25   (d) £50   (e) £500.

*7 Bill and Fagin are sent to prison. For how many years does each get sent down if their sentences are in the ratio 2 : 3 and total:
    (a) 5 years
    (b) 10 years
    (c) 15 years
    (d) 20 years?   Fig. 19:31   Bill's stretch   Fagin's stretch

8 Copy and complete the table for Figure 19:32.

Each time check that MX + XN = MN.

M   X   N
Fig. 19:32

Length of MN	20 cm	10 cm	12 cm	12 cm	16 cm	28 cm	27 cm	22 cm
MX : XN	7 : 3	3 : 2	5 : 1	1 : 5	5 : 3	3 : 4	5 : 4	3 : 8
Total parts	10							
Each part	2 cm							
MX	14 cm							
XN	6 cm							

9 Jane and Kim both have records in the ratio L.P.s to singles = 4 : 3.

(a) Jane has 49 records. How many are L.P.s?

(b) Kim has 35 records. How many are singles?

10 Jock, Iain and Sandy all like the ratio of their whisky to water to be 4 : 5. One evening Jock has 45 ml to drink, Iain has 108 ml and Sandy has 270 ml. How many millilitres of whisky does each drink?

11 Frank feeds his seals according to their age. A two-year-old seal is fed six fish. How many fish should a three-year-old seal receive?

12 Angela takes six steps to cross a room 4 metres wide. How wide is a room if she takes:
(a) 3 steps to cross   (b) 9 steps to cross?

13 Mr Mean pays all his workmen the same miserable bonus. He needs £100 to pay eight workmen. How much will he need to pay twelve workmen?

14 Draw the shapes in Figure 19:33 on squared paper, then draw larger shapes with the sides increased in the ratios given. Find the ratio of the areas for each pair of shapes.

2:1   3:2   3:2   4:3   4:3

Fig. 19:33

A Review

For Discussion

Figure 20:1 illustrates the fact that $\frac{3}{12} = \frac{1}{4}$ (three twelfths is the same as one quarter).

Fig. 20:1

Figure 20:2 illustrates the fact that $\frac{8}{12} = \frac{2}{3}$ (eight twelfths is the same as two thirds).

Fig. 20:2

What is illustrated in Figure 20:3?

(a)

(b)

(c)

(d)

Fig. 20:3

1 Figure 20:1 showed that $\frac{3}{12} = \frac{1}{4}$ or that $\frac{1}{4} = \frac{3}{12}$.

We can also show this by writing: $\frac{1}{4} = \frac{1 \times 3}{4 \times 3} = \frac{3}{12}$.

Both the top and the bottom numbers were multiplied by 3.

Similarly, $\frac{2}{3} = \frac{2 \times 4}{3 \times 4} = \frac{8}{12}$.

Show in a similar way that:

(a) $\frac{1}{6} = \frac{2}{12}$ (b) $\frac{3}{4} = \frac{9}{12}$ (c) $\frac{5}{6} = \frac{10}{12}$ (d) $\frac{3}{4} = \frac{12}{16}$.

2 By dividing the top and bottom numbers by the same number (usually called 'cancelling') write as simply as possible:

(a) $\frac{6}{8}$ (b) $\frac{8}{16}$ (c) $\frac{12}{15}$ (d) $\frac{12}{16}$ (e) $\frac{9}{30}$ (f) $\frac{24}{36}$ (g) $\frac{20}{48}$.

3 Example Change the top-heavy fraction $\frac{15}{6}$ to a mixed number.

$$\frac{15}{6} = 2\frac{3}{6} = 2\frac{1}{2}$$

Write as a mixed number:

(a) $\frac{13}{7}$ (b) $\frac{12}{5}$ (c) $\frac{18}{4}$ (d) $\frac{20}{6}$ (e) $\frac{28}{10}$ (f) $\frac{36}{15}$.

---

4 Draw patterns like Figures 20:1, 2 and 3 to show that:

(a) $\frac{10}{12} = \frac{5}{6}$ (b) $\frac{2}{16} = \frac{1}{8}$ (c) $\frac{4}{16} = \frac{1}{4}$ (d) $\frac{8}{16} = \frac{1}{2}$ (e) $\frac{12}{15} = \frac{4}{5}$.

5 Draw three 2 cm-sided equilateral triangles. Divide one into quarters, one into eighths and one into sixteenths. Draw two 3 cm-sided equilateral triangles. Divide one into ninths and the other into eighteenths. Use your triangles to illustrate some equivalent fractions.

B Addition and subtraction

8 eighths = 1 whole   3 eighths + 3 eighths + 3 eighths = 9 eighths

$$\frac{8}{8} = 1 \qquad\qquad \frac{3}{8} + \frac{3}{8} + \frac{3}{8} = \frac{9}{8} = 1\frac{1}{8}$$

Fig. 20:4

1 (a) $\frac{1}{4} + \frac{1}{4} + \frac{1}{4}$ (b) $\frac{1}{5} + \frac{1}{5}$ (c) $\frac{1}{7} + 3\frac{1}{7}$ (d) $4\frac{5}{7} + \frac{1}{7}$ (e) $2\frac{3}{5} + 3\frac{1}{5}$

2 (a) $\frac{3}{5} - \frac{1}{5}$ (b) $\frac{8}{11} - \frac{3}{11}$ (c) $3\frac{3}{11} - 3\frac{2}{11}$ (d) $6\frac{4}{9} - 4\frac{4}{9}$ (e) $8\frac{15}{16} - 2\frac{8}{16}$

3 Write as a whole or a mixed number:

(a) $\frac{12}{5}$ (b) $\frac{17}{4}$ (c) $\frac{20}{3}$ (d) $\frac{25}{5}$.

4 Write as a whole or a mixed number:

(a) $\frac{7}{4} + \frac{2}{4}$ (b) $\frac{14}{5} + \frac{3}{5}$ (c) $\frac{5}{7} + \frac{4}{7} + \frac{6}{7}$.

5 Give each answer to the following as simply as possible.

(a) $\frac{3}{4} + \frac{1}{4}$ (b) $\frac{1}{6} + \frac{2}{6}$ (c) $\frac{5}{8} + \frac{1}{8}$ (d) $\frac{4}{9} + \frac{2}{9}$ (e) $\frac{7}{8} + \frac{3}{8}$ (f) $\frac{7}{9} + \frac{5}{9}$

(g) $\frac{4}{6} + \frac{6}{6}$ (h) $\frac{7}{10} + \frac{7}{10}$ (i) $\frac{11}{12} + \frac{5}{12}$ (j) $\frac{5}{14} + \frac{15}{14}$ (k) $\frac{13}{15} + \frac{8}{15}$ (l) $\frac{25}{16} + \frac{25}{16}$

6 What has to be added to the following fractions to make a whole one?

(a) $\frac{1}{2}$ (b) $\frac{3}{4}$ (c) $\frac{1}{4}$ (d) $\frac{7}{8}$ (e) $\frac{3}{8}$ (f) $\frac{2}{7}$ (g) $\frac{11}{15}$ (h) $\frac{17}{100}$ (i) $\frac{28}{100}$

---

7 (a) $\frac{x}{5} + \frac{x}{5}$ (b) $\frac{y}{7} + \frac{2y}{7}$ (c) $\frac{3a}{4} + \frac{a}{4}$ (d) $\frac{3x}{6} + \frac{3x}{6}$ (e) $\frac{7x}{4} + \frac{x}{4}$ (f) $\frac{2}{a} + \frac{7}{a}$

     (g) $\frac{6}{w} - \frac{3}{w}$ (h) $\frac{9a}{x} - \frac{3a}{x}$ (i) $\frac{3k}{7y} - \frac{k}{7y}$ (j) $\frac{4h}{3a} - \frac{h}{3a}$

8 Design one tiling pattern, made up from square tiles, and able to illustrate the fractions $\frac{1}{2}, \frac{1}{3}, \frac{1}{4}, \frac{1}{6}, \frac{1}{9}$ and $\frac{1}{18}$.

Draw six copies of your pattern and show how many square tiles make each fraction of it. Then draw more copies to illustrate other fractions (like $\frac{5}{6}, \frac{3}{4}$ and $\frac{2}{9}$).

C   Different denominators

Fractions can be added and subtracted only when they are the same kind of fraction, that is when they have the same bottom number.

If the fractions have different bottom numbers one or both must be changed.

You can either change both bottom numbers to the lowest number that both will divide into (Method A) or use their product (Method B). Method B is easier to do, but you may need to simplify the answer fraction by cancelling.

Example 1 $\frac{5}{7} + \frac{1}{14}$

     Method A   The lowest number that 7 and 14 both divide into is 14.

                    5 sevenths is 10 fourteenths (multiplying both numbers by 2).

                    So: $\frac{5}{7} + \frac{1}{14} \rightarrow \frac{10}{14} + \frac{1}{14} = \frac{11}{14}$.

Method B $\quad \frac{5}{7} + \frac{1}{14} = \frac{70+7}{98} = \frac{77}{98} = \frac{11}{14}$.

Method B is better if you want to work the answer in your head, especially if the numbers are small.

Note the pattern of the three multiplications:

$$\frac{5}{7} \diagup\!\!\!\!\!\diagdown \frac{1}{14}$$

In algebraic terms we would write $\frac{a}{b} + \frac{c}{d} = \frac{ad+bc}{bd}$.

Example 2 $\quad \frac{5}{6} - \frac{3}{4}$

Method A $\quad \frac{5}{6} - \frac{3}{4} \rightarrow \frac{10}{12} - \frac{9}{12} = \frac{1}{12}$

Method B $\quad \frac{5}{6} - \frac{3}{4} = \frac{20-18}{24} = \frac{2}{24} = \frac{1}{12}$

1 Copy and complete:

(a) $\frac{2}{7} = \frac{2 \times 2}{7 \times 2} = \frac{}{14}$ (b) $\frac{3}{5} = \frac{3 \times}{5 \times} \quad = \frac{}{20}$.

2 Copy the following, replacing the letters by the correct numbers.

(a) $\frac{1}{2} = \frac{a}{8}$ (b) $\frac{1}{2} = \frac{b}{6}$ (c) $\frac{1}{2} = \frac{c}{16}$ (d) $\frac{1}{4} = \frac{d}{8}$ (e) $\frac{1}{4} = \frac{e}{12}$ (f) $\frac{1}{8} = \frac{f}{16}$

(g) $\frac{1}{8} = \frac{g}{80}$ (h) $\frac{1}{7} = \frac{h}{56}$

3 State the smallest number that can be divided exactly by:
(a) 3 and 4   (b) 2 and 4   (c) 3 and 7   (d) 3 and 9   (e) 4 and 6
(f) 4 and 10   (g) 8 and 10   (h) 6 and 8   (i) 6 and 12   (j) 5 and 7.

4 (a) $\frac{2}{7} + \frac{1}{2}$ (b) $\frac{4}{5} + \frac{1}{10}$ (c) $\frac{1}{4} + \frac{2}{3}$ (d) $\frac{5}{8} + \frac{5}{16}$ (e) $\frac{5}{9} - \frac{1}{6}$ (f) $\frac{7}{8} - \frac{5}{6}$

*5 Copy the following, replacing the letters by the correct numbers.

(a) $\frac{1}{3} = \frac{a}{6}$ (b) $\frac{1}{3} = \frac{b}{9}$ (c) $\frac{1}{5} = \frac{c}{15}$ (d) $\frac{1}{6} = \frac{d}{18}$ (e) $\frac{2}{3} = \frac{e}{6}$

(f) $\frac{2}{3} = \frac{f}{9}$ (g) $\frac{2}{5} = \frac{g}{10}$ (h) $\frac{2}{5} = \frac{h}{20}$

*6 (a) $\frac{1}{5} + \frac{1}{4}$ (b) $\frac{1}{2} + \frac{1}{8}$ (c) $\frac{1}{7} + \frac{1}{2}$ (d) $\frac{1}{6} + \frac{1}{5}$ (e) $\frac{1}{4} + \frac{1}{3}$ (f) $\frac{1}{4} + \frac{1}{6}$

*7 (a) $\frac{1}{6} + \frac{1}{8}$ (b) $\frac{1}{6} + \frac{1}{9}$ (c) $\frac{1}{8} + \frac{1}{10}$ (d) $\frac{2}{5} + \frac{1}{4}$ (e) $\frac{3}{7} + \frac{1}{2}$ (f) $\frac{1}{6} + \frac{3}{5}$

*8 (a) $\frac{3}{8} - \frac{1}{4}$ (b) $\frac{4}{9} - \frac{1}{4}$ (c) $\frac{5}{7} - \frac{1}{2}$ (d) $\frac{5}{6} - \frac{3}{8}$

9 Write answers to the following as simply as possible. If the answer is a top-heavy fraction change it to a mixed number.

    (a) $\frac{11}{12} + \frac{1}{4}$ (b) $\frac{7}{16} + \frac{3}{8}$ (c) $\frac{3}{4} + \frac{5}{6}$ (d) $\frac{7}{9} + \frac{7}{18}$ (e) $\frac{2}{7} + \frac{8}{21}$

    (f) $\frac{7}{8} + \frac{4}{5}$ (g) $\frac{8}{15} + \frac{2}{3} + \frac{1}{5}$ (h) $\frac{5}{6} + \frac{5}{12} + \frac{1}{4}$

10 A string of numbers may be added in any order. For example, $3 + 4 + 9 + 7$ is the same as $3 + 9 + 4 + 7$.

As $2\frac{3}{4}$ is $2 + \frac{3}{4}$, and $3\frac{1}{2}$ is $3 + \frac{1}{2}$ we can write $2\frac{3}{4} + 3\frac{1}{2}$ as $2 + \frac{3}{4} + 3 + \frac{1}{2}$, then re-arrange these to $2 + 3 + \frac{3}{4} + \frac{1}{2} = 5\frac{5}{4} = 6\frac{1}{4}$.

So when adding or subtracting mixed numbers you can deal with the whole numbers first, then work out the fraction part.

Find:
    (a) $1\frac{1}{2} + 1\frac{1}{4}$ (b) $2\frac{1}{4} + 3\frac{3}{4}$ (c) $4\frac{1}{2} + 3\frac{3}{4}$ (d) $1\frac{1}{5} + 2\frac{4}{5}$ (e) $4\frac{7}{16} - \frac{3}{8}$

    (f) $2\frac{4}{5} - \frac{3}{7}$ (g) $3\frac{25}{33} - 1\frac{8}{11}$ (h) $4\frac{13}{16} - 2\frac{7}{12}$.

11 Find the missing fraction, written as simply as possible:

    (a) $\frac{2}{3} + \quad = \frac{5}{6}$ (b) $\frac{1}{3} + \quad = \frac{5}{9}$ (c) $\frac{1}{4} + \quad = \frac{11}{12}$ (d) $\frac{1}{6} + \quad = \frac{13}{18}$

    (e) $\frac{5}{12} + \quad = \frac{19}{36}$

12 Anna had to do some lines. She did a half of them on Monday and a fifth of them on Tuesday.

    (a) What is the smallest number of lines she could have had?

    (b) What fraction of them had she done by Tuesday?

    (c) What fraction did she still have to do?

13 I spend a fifth of my income on the mortgage and two-thirds on housekeeping expenses.

    (a) What fraction is left?

    (b) If my income is £300 how much is spent on the mortgage and how much is spent on the housekeeping?

14 My garden has $200 \, \text{m}^2$ of lawn and $400 \, \text{m}^2$ for flowers and vegetables. What fraction of my garden is lawn?

15 Samir gives $\frac{1}{3}$ of his sweets to Diana and eats $\frac{5}{9}$ of them.

If he eats four more than he gives to Diana how many has he left?

---

16 Using a calculator for common fractions

Most calculators are not very useful for this type of question as they work in decimal fractions. However they can be used if a decimal fraction answer is acceptable.

Try: To find $4\frac{3}{4} + 1\frac{1}{8}$.

Four and three-quarters plus one and one-eighth

4 $\boxed{+}$ 3 $\boxed{\div}$ 4 $\boxed{+}$ 1 $\boxed{+}$ 1 $\boxed{\div}$ 8 $\boxed{=}$

If your calculator 'knows' the BODMAS rule, and works out division before addition, you will obtain the correct answer of 5.875 (i.e. $5\frac{7}{8}$). Make sure you really understand why the key sequence was as given, then work some of the exercise using your calculator.

If your answer is wrong (probably 0.46875) your calculator does not follow the BODMAS system. There is no easy way round this, but many not so easy ones!

Here is one using the accumulating memory ($\boxed{M+}$).

Make sure the memory is cancelled before you begin.

$\boxed{MC}$ 4 $\boxed{M+}$ 3 $\boxed{\div}$ 4 $\boxed{=}$ $\boxed{M+}$ 1 $\boxed{M+}$ 1 $\boxed{\div}$ 8 $\boxed{=}$ $\boxed{M+}$ $\boxed{MR}$

| Store contents | 0 | 4 | | $4\frac{3}{4}$ | $4\frac{3}{4} + 1$ | | $4\frac{3}{4} + 1\frac{1}{8}$ |

D Subtraction; harder examples

Example $3\frac{3}{5} - 1\frac{3}{4}$

Method A $\quad 3\frac{3}{5} - 1\frac{3}{4} \rightarrow 2\frac{12-15}{20} \rightarrow 2 - \frac{3}{20} = 1\frac{17}{20}$

Method B $\quad 3\frac{3}{5} - 1\frac{3}{4} \rightarrow 2\frac{12-15}{20} \rightarrow 1\frac{20+12-15}{20} = 1\frac{17}{20}$

1 (a) $1 - \frac{1}{7}$ (b) $1 - \frac{2}{7}$ (c) $1 - \frac{4}{9}$ (d) $1 - \frac{3}{11}$ (e) $2 - \frac{1}{5}$ (f) $7 - \frac{2}{9}$

2 (a) $6 - 7$ (b) $8 - 9$ (c) $9 - 11$ (d) $4 - 10$

3 (a) $6\frac{3}{8} + 1\frac{1}{4}$ (b) $6\frac{3}{8} - 1\frac{1}{4}$ (c) $4\frac{1}{2} + 2\frac{1}{7}$ (d) $4\frac{1}{2} - 2\frac{1}{7}$

4 (a) $3\frac{1}{6} - \frac{1}{4}$ (b) $4\frac{1}{3} - \frac{2}{5}$ (c) $2\frac{2}{3} - \frac{5}{6}$ (d) $3\frac{3}{4} - \frac{4}{5}$ (e) $2\frac{3}{8} - 1\frac{3}{4}$
   (f) $4\frac{5}{8} - 1\frac{15}{16}$ (g) $2\frac{1}{5} - 1\frac{7}{10}$ (h) $8\frac{5}{9} - 3\frac{11}{12}$

*5 (a) $2\frac{1}{3} - \frac{1}{2}$ (b) $3\frac{1}{3} - \frac{1}{2}$ (c) $4\frac{1}{4} - \frac{1}{2}$ (d) $3\frac{3}{4} - \frac{7}{8}$ (e) $2\frac{3}{4} - 1\frac{7}{8}$
   (f) $4\frac{1}{5} - 1\frac{3}{10}$ (g) $7\frac{1}{5} - 4\frac{7}{10}$ (h) $6\frac{9}{16} - 3\frac{7}{8}$

6 Answer (a) and (b) for each triangle in Figure 20:5.

(a) Measure the marked angle.

(b) How many times as long as each upright line is the sloping one?

(i)   (ii) 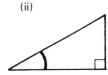   (iii)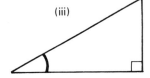

Fig. 20:5

7 Use your answer to question 6(b) to calculate a, b, c and d in Figure 20:6.

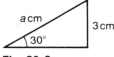 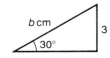 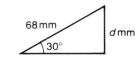

Fig. 20:6

8 In Figure 20:7 calculate (without drawing) the vertical height of the kite.

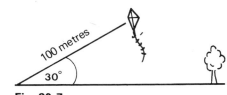

Fig. 20:7

9 Draw Figure 20:8 accurately, full size.

Measure AC and show that AB:AC ≒ 7:10.

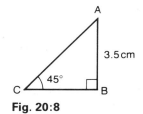

Fig. 20:8

10 Using the result you found in question 9 calculate *a*, *b*, *c* and *d* in Figure 20:9.

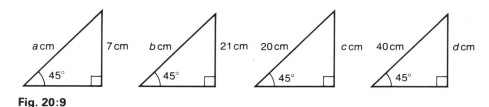

Fig. 20:9

11 Construct the triangles in Figure 20:9 accurately and so check your answers to question 10.

---

12 Investigate the sum of the infinite series that starts: $\frac{1}{2} + \frac{1}{4} + \frac{1}{8} + \frac{1}{16} + \ldots$

13 Investigate other infinite series, e.g. $\frac{1}{2} - \frac{1}{4} + \frac{1}{8} - \frac{1}{16} \ldots$ and $\frac{1}{2} + \frac{1}{3} + \frac{1}{4} + \frac{1}{5} + \ldots$

14 Program a computer to help you answer questions 12 and 13.

21 Equations: linear

A Solving equations (i)

Equations where the letter only appears once are best solved by the 'logic' approach, that is by thinking out what number must be used instead of the letter to make the equation true. This method is often called 'solving by inspection'.

For example, if $n + 7 = -3$, then n must be -10 as $-10 + 7 = -3$.

You can instead use the 'balance' or 'change-sides' method. Your teacher will explain it fully. The following examples show you how to write the solutions.

$$n + 8 = 10 \qquad\qquad 4n = 12 \qquad\qquad 6 - n = 1$$
$$n \quad = 10 - 8 \qquad\quad n = \tfrac{12}{4} \qquad\qquad -n = 1 - 6$$
$$n \quad = 2 \qquad\qquad\quad n = 3 \qquad\qquad -n = -5$$
$$\qquad\qquad\qquad\qquad\qquad\qquad\qquad\qquad n = 5$$

In questions 1 to 11 solve the equations to find the values of n.

1 (a) $n + 4 = 8$ (b) $n + 9 = 23$ (c) $5 + n = 13$ (d) $4 + n = 4$ (e) $7 + n = 0$
   (f) $13 + n = 6$

2 (a) $n - 9 = 16$ (b) $n - 13 = 42$ (c) $n - 73 = 91$

3 (a) $3n = 6$ (b) $7n = 56$ (c) $2n = -8$ (d) $5n = -15$

*4 (a) $n + 3 = 7$ (b) $n + 5 = 12$ (c) $2 + n = 9$ (d) $4 + n = 13$

*5 (a) $n + 5 = 1$ (b) $7 + n = 6$ (c) $8 + n = 0$

*6 (a) $n - 4 = 11$ (b) $n - 8 = 17$ (c) $n - 8 = 12$

*7 (a) $5n = 20$ (b) $9n = 72$ (c) $7n = -14$ (d) $8n = -64$

8 (a) $3 - n = 2$ (b) $17 - n = 8$ (c) $24 - n = 15$ (d) $5 - n = 0$

9 (a) $4 - n = 7$ (b) $5 - n = 8$ (c) $16 - n = 17$ (d) $9 - n = 11$

10 (a) $n + 7 = -4$ (b) $n + 5 = -3$ (c) $n + 6 = -8$

11 In algebra work, improper fractions (top-heavy fractions) are usually not changed to mixed numbers.

Solve:
(a) $3n = 5$ (b) $6n = 7$ (c) $2n = 1$ (d) $4n = 3$ (e) $3n = 1$ (f) $5n = 2$
(g) $4n = 7$ (h) $3n = 10$.

12 $x \geqslant 3$ means 'x is 3 or more'. (Literally: x is bigger than or equal to 3.)

Inequalities can be solved like equations.

Example $x - 1 \geqslant 5 \rightarrow x \geqslant 6$

Compare this with $x - 1 = 5 \rightarrow x = 6$.

Solve:
(a) $x + 4 \geqslant 9$ (b) $x - 8 \geqslant 2$ (c) $3 + d \geqslant 9$ (d) $4 + f \geqslant 2$
(e) $5 - x \leqslant 5$ (Think!)   (f) $7 - w \leqslant 7$.

13 Solve:
(a) $4x \geqslant 8$ (b) $8x \geqslant 4$ (c) $5n > 10$ (d) $5e < 10$.

14 If x is an integer, list the set of possible values of x if:

(a) $6 < 2x < 10$ (that is, $2x > 6$ and also $2x < 10$, so $x > 3$ and $x < 5$)

(b) $8 < 2x < 12$ (c) $8 \leqslant 2x \leqslant 12$ (d) $16 \leqslant 4x \leqslant 36$.

15

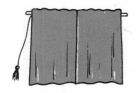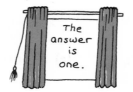

Fig. 21:1

(a) Think of a number. Add 3. Multiply by 2. Subtract 4. Divide by 2. Subtract the number you first thought of.

(b) Repeat part (a) for a different starting number.

(c) You can find out why this works by using a letter for the number, say n.

$$n \xrightarrow{+3} n + 3 \xrightarrow{\times 2} 2n + 6 \xrightarrow{-4} 2n + 2 \xrightarrow{\div 2} n + 1 \xrightarrow{-n} 1.$$

16 In the following, work out the answers for several numbers then illustrate the result using algebra.

    (a) Think of a number. Multiply it by 2. Add 16. Divide by 2. Subtract the number you first thought of.

    (b) Think of a number. Multiply it by 2. Add 3. Multiply by 5. Subtract 6. Cross out the units digit.

17 Now make up a series of instructions for yourself, so that the answer is always the number you first thought of.

    Explain by algebra why it works.

18 Investigate an inequality statement like $13 > 12$ to find out what you can and cannot do to both sides of an inequality without making it untrue.

B   Solving equations (ii)

Example   Solve $3x + 2 = 14$

$$3x + 2 = 14 \rightarrow 3x = 12 \rightarrow x = 4$$

In questions 1 to 9 solve the equations to find the values of n.

1 (a) $2n + 1 = 7$ (b) $3n + 2 = 11$ (c) $4n + 3 = 11$

2 (a) $4n - 3 = 9$ (b) $3n - 8 = 10$ (c) $8n - 7 = 9$

3 (a) $2n + 3 = 1$ (b) $4n + 15 = 7$ (c) $6n + 13 = 31$

*4 (a) $3n + 5 = 11$ (b) $2n + 7 = 15$ (c) $4n + 1 = 21$

*5 (a) $7n - 2 = 5$ (b) $6n - 7 = 17$ (c) $9n - 9 = 9$

*6 (a) $4n + 7 = 3$ (b) $5n + 11 = 1$ (c) $3n + 17 = 2$

7 (a) $3n - 3 = 0$ (b) $7n + 14 = 0$ (c) $5n + 3 = -2$ (d) $2n + 8 = -8$

8 (a) $7n = -35$ (b) $8n = 56$ (c) $56n = 8$ (d) $9n = 63$

9 (a) $13n + 8 = 8$ (b) $7n + 1 = 2$ (c) $3n - 2 = -1$

10 Changing the subject

Example   If $y = x + 2$ then y is the *subject*.

If $y = x + 2$ then $x = y - 2$. Now x is the subject.

Change the subject to x if:
(a) $y = x + 3$ (b) $y = x - 2$ (c) $y = x + 6$ (d) $y = x - 3g$
(e) $y = 4 + x$ (f) $y = 3 - x$ (g) $y = 2 - x$ (h) $y = a - x$
(i) $y = 2k - x$ (j) $y = 2x$ (k) $y = 3x$ (l) $y = 2x - 8$.

11 Complete exercise 21A questions 12 to 14 before doing this question.

Solve the following inequalities.
(a) $3x + 5 \geqslant 8$ (b) $3x + 5 < 8$ (c) $2x - 7 \leqslant 9$ (d) $5x - 9 > 6$
(e) $2x + 1 < 2$ (f) $3x - 2 < 0$

12 If n is an even number, what kind of a number is:
(a) $n + 1$ (b) $n + 2$ (c) $2n$ (d) $2n + 1$ (e) $2n + 2$?

13 Use algebra to prove:
(a) even + even = even   (b) odd + odd = even.

14 Add together any five consecutive integers. Divide the answer by 5, then take away 2. Prove your result by algebra. (Start: $n + n + 1 + n + 2 + ...$)

15 Find a rule to work out the first number if a friend tells you the sum of three consecutive integers.

16 Work out by algebra how to find the number that your friend thought of if she: multiplies it by 5, adds 3, multiplies by 4, adds 8, multiplies by 5 and then tells you her answer.

17 Trial and improvement

Example   Solve $x^2 + x = 15$

Try $x = 5$ Key 5 ⊠ 5 ⊞ 5 ⊟   30 Too big.
Try $x = 3$ 12 Too small.
Try $x = 3.5$ Key 3 ⊠ 3 ⊞ 3 ⊟   15.75 Too big.
Try $x = 3.4$ 14.96 Bit too small,
Try $x = 3.42$ etc.

There is another solution to the example. Can you find it, correct to 2 decimal places?

18 Solve:
(a) $x^2 - x = 15$ (two solutions)   (b) $2x^2 + x = 5$ (two solutions)

(c) $x^3 = 10$ (one solution)   (d) $\dfrac{1}{x} + x = 20$ (two solutions)

22 Special quadrilaterals

A Naming special quadrilaterals

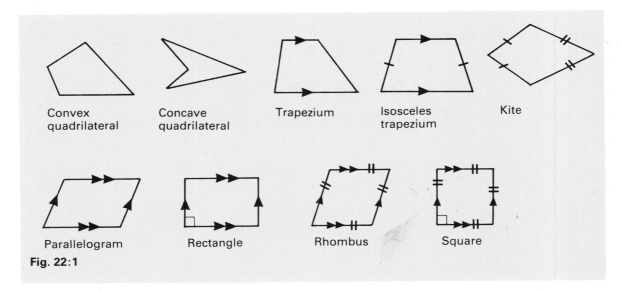

Fig. 22:1

1 Name the quadrilaterals in Figure 22:2.

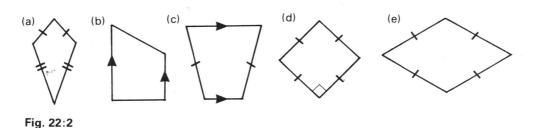

Fig. 22:2

*2 Cut strips of card, four 6 cm long and 1 cm wide, and two 4 cm long and 1 cm wide.

Join four of the strips with 'point-up' drawing-pins to make each of the seven special quadrilaterals (from trapezium to square) in Figure 22:1.

3 Calculate the angles of a quadrilateral if:

(a) they are all the same size   (b) three are equal and the fourth is 18°

(c) two are equal and the other two are each 97°

(d) they are in the ratio 1:2:3:4. (Hint: split 360° into this ratio.)

(e) they are in the ratio 2:3:3:4   (f) they are in the ratio 1:1:3:4.

4 What special quadrilaterals must those in question 3 parts (a), (c), (e) and (f) be? Note: (a) has two answers; (c) has three answers; (e) has ~~two~~ one answers; (f) has one answer. Sketch an example of each quadrilateral, showing the size of each angle.

5 Find whether the angle sum of a concave quadrilateral is also 360°.

6 Use the method shown in Figure 22:3 to construct a square equal in area to a rectangle. The points are found in alphabetical order. Measure your construction to check that the areas are equal. Repeat until you know it.

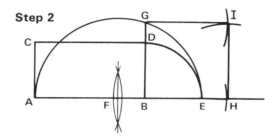

Step 1

Step 2

Fig. 22:3

B   Side and angle properties

Figure 22:4 shows that a parallelogram has its opposite sides equal and its opposite angles equal.

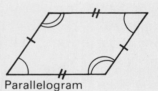

Fig. 22:4   Parallelogram

1 Draw neatly and accurately the seven special quadrilaterals (trapezium to square) in Figure 22:1. Mark on each figure its equal sides and angles.

*2 Copy the following sentences and complete them with the names of the quadrilaterals described. No two answers are the same.

(a) A . . . has one pair of parallel sides, the other sides being unequal.

(b) An . . . has one pair of parallel sides, the other sides being equal.

(c) A . . . has no parallel sides, but has two different pairs of equal sides.

(d) A . . . has two pairs of parallel sides and two pairs of equal sides, but no right angles.

(e) A . . . is a parallelogram with right angles and different-length adjacent sides.

(f) A . . . is a parallelogram with all sides equal but no right angles.

(g) A . . . is a rhombus with right angles.

3 If you did question 2 go straight on to question 4.

✗ Otherwise read question 2 and name the quadrilaterals, but do not copy the sentences.

4 Name *all* the special quadrilaterals that could be described as follows. The number of answers possible is given in brackets.

(a) four equal sides (2)   (b) four right angles (2)

(c) two different pairs of equal sides (3)   (d) only one pair of parallel sides (2)

(e) only two equal sides (1)

(f) two different pairs of equal sides but no parallel sides (1)

(g) four equal angles (2)

(h) two different pairs of equal angles in opposite corners (2)

(i) two different pairs of equal angles, not 90° (3)

(j) only one pair of equal angles (2)

---

5 Copy Figure 22:5 in which ABCD is a parallelo-gram, angle D is 30° and AD = AE. Calculate angles ABC, AED, DAE and AEC, giving reasons chosen from the following list.

(Angle sum of triangle); (Opposite angles of parallelogram); (Isosceles triangle); (Adjacent angles on a straight line).

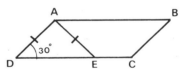

Fig. 22:5

6 Copy Figure 22:6, in which ABCD is a parallelogram, AC = AB and ∠ B = 70°.

(a) Why must △ ACD be isosceles?

(b) Calculate angles ACB, BAC, ADC, DAC and ACD. Give clear reasons chosen from the list in question 5.

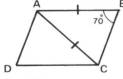

Fig. 22:6

7 Draw any quadrilateral. Cut it out. Join the midpoints of its sides to make another quadrilateral. What shape is it? Cut off the four triangles. Will they fit inside the quadrilateral? Repeat for other quadrilaterals. Can you prove your results?

C   Diagonals

AC and BD are the diagonals of square ABCD.

They are equal, bisect each other, and cross at 90°.

They bisect the corner angles and cut the square into four congruent triangles.

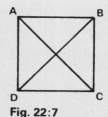

Fig. 22:7

1 By drawing neat accurate diagrams, find which special quadrilaterals have:

(a) equal diagonals (3 answers)

(b) diagonals crossing at right angles (3 answers)

(c) diagonals bisecting each other (cutting each other in half) (4 answers).

*2 Draw large accurate diagrams of each of the special quadrilaterals (trapezium to square) in Figure 22:1. Draw the diagonals on each and mark all the equal lines, as in Figure 22:8.

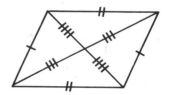

Parallelogram
Fig. 22:8

*3 Repeat question 2 but this time mark all the equal angles, as in Figure 22:9.

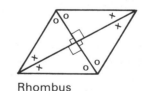

Rhombus
Fig. 22:9

4 AXC and BXD are two straight lines crossing at X to make a right angle. Draw sketches of the two lines and name the figure made by joining A, B, C and D if:

(a) AX = BX = CX = DX

(b) AX = CX, BX = DX, but AX ≠ BX

(c) AX = CX, but BX ≠ DX.

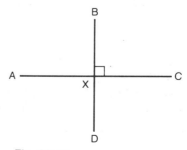

Fig. 22:10

5 Copy the quadrilateral 'family tree' in Figure 22:11.

Fill in the names of the special quadrilaterals.

Each quadrilateral has all the properties of its 'ancestors'.

Key: // means parallel; ⊥ means perpendicular (at right angles).

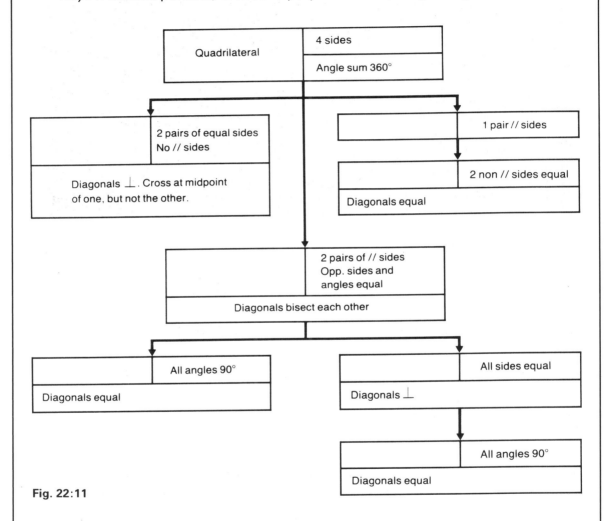

| Quadrilateral | 4 sides |
| | Angle sum 360° |

| | 2 pairs of equal sides No // sides |
| Diagonals ⊥. Cross at midpoint of one, but not the other. | |

	1 pair // sides
	2 non // sides equal
Diagonals equal	

| | 2 pairs of // sides Opp. sides and angles equal |
| Diagonals bisect each other | |

| | All angles 90° |
| Diagonals equal | |

| | All sides equal |
| Diagonals ⊥ | |

| | All angles 90° |
| Diagonals equal | |

Fig. 22:11

6 A rhombus ABCD has diagonals of length 12 cm and 8 cm, crossing at X. Draw a diagram of the rhombus, then calculate the areas of triangles AXB, AXD, CXD and BXC. Finally calculate the area of the rhombus.

Using your calculator

Using water

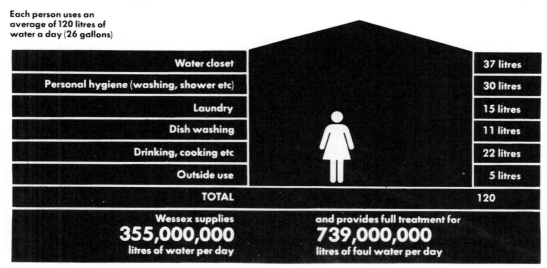

USE OF WATER IN THE HOME

Each person uses an
average of 120 litres of
water a day (26 gallons)

Water closet	37 litres
Personal hygiene (washing, shower etc)	30 litres
Laundry	15 litres
Dish washing	11 litres
Drinking, cooking etc	22 litres
Outside use	5 litres
TOTAL	120

Wessex supplies
355,000,000
litres of water per day

and provides full treatment for
739,000,000
litres of foul water per day

Use the above information and your calculator to answer the following questions.

1 How many litres is one gallon, correct to 3 decimal places?

2 How many gallons of water does the Authority supply each day?

3 About how many people live in the Authority's area?

4 In a year, how much water would an average person use:
(a) in litres   (b) in gallons?

5 If drinking/cooking water, which must be pure, were supplied separately from the rest, how many litres of purified water would the Authority need to supply each day?

6 If a man lives for 70 years, about how many gallons of water will he use:
(a) washing himself   (b) washing his clothes   (c) flushing the toilet?

7 It would save the Authority a lot of money if they only had to purify drinking/cooking water. Suggest reasons why this is not done.

8 Find the number of litres used to fill your school swimming pool, or one in your area.

A Review

> Key figure 5 or more: increase figure in front of it by 1.

For Discussion

How many numbers can you find in the newspaper articles shown in Figure 23:1 (which all appeared on the front page of *The Daily Telegraph* one day in October 1983)? Which of the numbers are exact and which are approximate? How approximate are the latter ones?

'Cure' in Caribbean for delinquents

By DAVID FLETCHER Health Services Correspondent

YOUNG delinquents from London are being sent for rehabilitation to the Caribbean island of St Vincent at a cost to ratepayers of £250 a week each, it was revealed yesterday.

Two Labour-controlled London councils, Lewisham and Camden, have sent a group of teenagers, all of whom are in local authority care, to an experimental school in St Vincent where they will stay for a full year.

Mr Michael Ward, an official of Lewisham Council, said: "In no way can we be said to be squandering ratepayers' money because it is cheaper to send the boys to St Vincent than it is to look after them at home.

"To keep them in a residential community home in this country would cost about £500 a week whereas the charges in St Vincent are £250 a week plus the cost of airfare—say about £300 a week in all.

Earlier this year Labour-controlled Islington council sent 14 unemployed black teenagers to Grenada for a six-week working holiday financed by a £3,250 grant from the council.

AMERICAN 'QUAKE

By Our New York Staff

A moderate earthquake registering 5·2 Richter and centred near Blue Mountain Lake, a village about 65 miles north of Albany, New York, brought no immediate reports of injury or serious damage.

U.S. JOBLESS RATE DOWN

By Our Washington Staff

American unemployment dropped to 9·3 per cent. last month from 9·5 per cent. in August as the resurgent economy provided nearly 400,000 new jobs, the Labour Department reported yesterday.

The new rate is the lowest in 17 months, and the Business Council, a group of 200 top executives, forecast that expansion should continue through 1984. Some 10,400,000 Americans are still looking for work, however.

DRIVER KISSED BY PASSENGER LOST CONTROL

A motorist driving home a woman he had just met at a party was so surprised when she suddenly kissed him that he lost control of the car, careered into a cul-de-sac and shunted one parked car into another.

Fig. 23:1

1 Approximate each of the following to the nearest thousand.
(a) 3124   (b) 7146   (c) 6365   (d) 1086   (e) 7893   (f) 7096
(g) 4986   (h) 5992   (i) 3999   (j) 999

2 Approximate the numbers in question 1 to the nearest hundred.

3 Approximate the numbers in question 1 to the nearest ten.

*4 State the key figure when approximating:
(a) 3126 to the nearest ten
(b) 4276 to the nearest hundred
(c) 3562 to the nearest thousand
(d) 1983 to the nearest thousand
(e) 1993 to the nearest hundred
(f) 1998 to the nearest ten.

*5 Approximate the numbers in question 4 as instructed.

*6 Approximate to the nearest hundred:
(a) 6247   (b) 7906   (c) 3150   (d) 4291   (e) 1993   (f) 2995.

7 Round each of the following so that there is only one figure in your answer that is not a zero.

Examples $7621 \rightarrow 8000;\quad 631 \rightarrow 600$

(a) 7291   (b) 934   (c) 899   (d) 571   (e) 981   (f) 955

8 By rounding each number as in question 7 we can easily find approximate answers to quite difficult questions.

Example $\dfrac{8917 \times 98}{261 \times 342} \rightarrow \dfrac{9000 \times 100}{300 \times 300}$

This can be cancelled: $\dfrac{\overset{10}{\cancel{9000}} \times 100}{\cancel{300} \times \cancel{300}}$

leaving the approximate answer as 10.

Find an approximate answer to:

(a) $\dfrac{512 \times 39}{51}$ (b) $\dfrac{59 \times 199}{309}$ (c) $\dfrac{6817 \times 24}{99}$

(d) $\dfrac{291 \times 799}{55 \times 360}$ (e) $\dfrac{8500 \times 19}{435}$ (f) $\dfrac{79 \times 5099}{999}$

9 Use a calculator to work out the answers to question 8 as exactly as possible.

Using the formula: Percentage error = error ÷ correct answer × 100, calculate the percentage error made by each approximation.

10 What is your age to the nearest year; to the nearest month; to the nearest day; to the nearest hour (minute?)?

A calculator and a mum with a good memory will help you!

At the 3rd pip you will be 12 years old precisely!

B Decimal places

Decimal fractions are often approximated to a number of decimal places; that is, the number stops after the stated number of figures after the decimal point. The last figure is 'rounded' as you have learnt to do with whole numbers.

Examples   304.5899 is 304.6 to 1 decimal place (or 1 d.p.)
The key figure is 8, so the 5 is rounded up to a 6.

304.5899 is 304.590 to 3 d.p.
The last 0 is needed to show that we *have* rounded to three figures after the decimal point.

Discuss   Is 304.59 the same as 304.590?

1 **Example**   16.83 is 1 ten, 6 units, 8 tenths, and 3 hundredths.

State the value of the figures in:
(a) 1.46   (b) 0.217   (c) 65.09

2 Write the numbers (a) to (c) in question 1 correct to one decimal place (1 d.p.).

3 Round, correct to 1 decimal place (1 d.p.):
(a) 6.173   (b) 4.238   (c) 3.127   (d) 91.949   (e) 91.964   (f) 9.999

4 Round the numbers in question 3 correct to 2 d.p.

*5 State the key figure when rounding to 2 decimal places (the nearest hundredth) in:
(a) 8.623   (b) 4.1856   (c) 3.2917   (d) 3.667   (e) 4.792   (f) 4.7951
(g) 3.22987   (h) 2.99961

*6 Round the numbers in question 5 correct to 2 d.p.

*7 Round the numbers in question 5 correct to 3 d.p.

8 Write as a decimal fraction, giving the answers correct to 3 d.p.
(a) 1.21×3.48 (b) $7.6 \div 3$ (c) $4.81 \div 7$ (d) $\frac{1}{3}$ (e) $\frac{1}{16}$ (f) $\frac{1}{32}$

9 **Example**   7.8695 metres is 7.870 metres to the nearest mm.

Write in metres, correct to the nearest mm and to the nearest cm:
(a) 1.2342 metres   (b) 2.7908 metres   (c) 2.2446 metres.

10 Write in grams correct to the nearest (i) mg   (ii) cg   (iii) g:
(a) 16.07811 g   (b) 93.9982 g   (c) 94.8545 g.

11 What is the shortest and longest possible for:

(a) the length of a nail, 3 cm long to the nearest cm

(b) the distance from my house to Yeovil, if it is 20 km to the nearest $\frac{1}{2}$ km?

---

12 Figure 23:2 shows a Vernier scale. It can be used to measure to the nearest mm although the bottom divisions are 10 mm apart and the top ones are 9 mm apart. Make one.

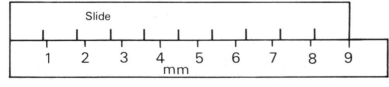

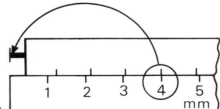

Fig. 23:2

13 Make a Vernier scale to read to $\frac{1}{2}$ mm. Make the divisions 5 mm and $4\frac{1}{2}$ mm.

For Discussion

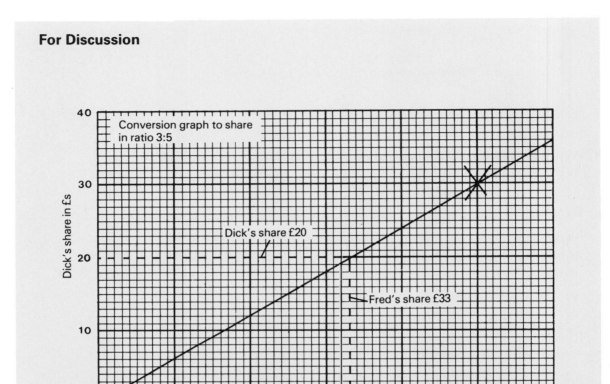

Fig. 24:1

1 (a) 1 inch is about 2.5 cm. About how many centimetres are 4 inches?

(b) Draw a conversion graph for inches to centimetres.
Use scales: Horizontal axis: centimetres, 0 to 13, 1 cm to 1 cm
Vertical axis: inches, 0 to 5, 2 cm to 1 inch

(c) Use your graph to change 1 cm, 2 cm, 3 cm, etc. (up to 12 cm) to inches, correct to the nearest tenth of an inch.

2 (a) 10 kg is about 22 lb ('pounds weight'). About how many lb are 50 kg?

(b) Draw a conversion graph for lb to kg.
Use scales: Horizontal axis: lb, 0 to 140, 1 cm to 10 lb
Vertical axis: kg, 0 to 50, 2 cm to 10 kg

(c) Use your graph to change 10 lb, 20 lb, 30 lb, etc. (up to 110 lb) and 112 lb (one hundredweight or 1 cwt) into kg to the nearest kg.

In questions 3 to 6 draw conversion graphs using the given scales. Always find a point as far away from the origin as possible when you draw your line.

3 Miles per hour (m.p.h.) to kilometres per hour (km/h). 100 km/h ≏ 62 m.p.h.

Horizontal: m.p.h., 0 to 140, 1 cm to 10 m.p.h.

Vertical: km/h, 0 to 200, 1 cm to 20 km/h

(a) Change to km/h: (i) 12 m.p.h. (ii) 22 m.p.h. (iii) 82 m.p.h.

(b) Change to m.p.h.: (i) 84 km/h (ii) 120 km/h (iii) 136 km/h.

4 Marks out of 65 ($M/65$) to percentage marks ($M\%$).

Horizontal: $M/65$, 0 to 65, 1 cm to 5 marks.

Vertical: $M\%$, 0 to 100, 1 cm to 10 marks.

Change to percentage marks:
(a) $\frac{4}{65}$ (b) $\frac{26}{65}$ (c) $\frac{39}{65}$ (d) $\frac{53}{65}$ (e) $\frac{63}{65}$.

5 Degrees Celcius (centigrade), °C, to degrees Fahrenheit, °F.

0°C = 32°F; 100°C = 212°F

Horizontal: °F, −40 to 220, 1 cm to 20°F

Vertical: °C, −40 to 100, 1 cm to 10°C

Note: Be careful. The line goes through (32, 0) *not* (0,0).

(a) Change to °F: (i) 5°C (ii) 17°C (iii) 82°C.

(b) Change to °C: (i) 50°F (ii) 70°F (iii) 180°F.

6 Deutschmarks (DM) to £s (on March 30, 1984). £1 = DM 3.70

Horizontal: DM, 0 to 25, 2 cm to 5 DM.

Vertical: £s, 0 to 5, 2 cm to £1.

Change to DM, correct to the nearest 0.25 DM:
(a) £1.60 (b) £2.30 (c) £3.10 (d) 80p (e) £1.15 (f) £4.80

7 My car's petrol tank holds 9 gallons. Design a suitable conversion graph from litres to gallons (11 gallons is almost exactly 50 litres).

8 Draw a conversion graph for 'Revolutions turned by the minute-hand of a clock' to 'Angle turned by the hour-hand'.

25 Vectors

A Position vectors

Figure 25:1 shows the position vector:

$\begin{pmatrix} 3 \\ 2 \end{pmatrix}$ going 3 forwards and 2 up.

$\begin{pmatrix} 3 \\ -2 \end{pmatrix}$ going 3 forwards and 2 down.

$\begin{pmatrix} -3 \\ 2 \end{pmatrix}$ going 3 backwards and 2 up.

$\begin{pmatrix} -3 \\ -2 \end{pmatrix}$ going 3 backwards and 2 down.

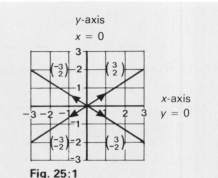

Fig. 25:1

1 On 1 cm-squared paper draw and label axes from −5 to 5 each.

2 Using the axes you have drawn, draw the position vectors:

$\begin{pmatrix} 5 \\ 3 \end{pmatrix}$; $\begin{pmatrix} 5 \\ 1 \end{pmatrix}$; $\begin{pmatrix} 2 \\ 4 \end{pmatrix}$; $\begin{pmatrix} -2 \\ 4 \end{pmatrix}$; $\begin{pmatrix} -5 \\ 1 \end{pmatrix}$; $\begin{pmatrix} -5 \\ -1 \end{pmatrix}$; $\begin{pmatrix} -2 \\ -4 \end{pmatrix}$; $\begin{pmatrix} 2 \\ -4 \end{pmatrix}$; $\begin{pmatrix} 5 \\ -1 \end{pmatrix}$.

Remember the arrows!

3 **Example** The vector representing a move of 4 back and 3 up is $\begin{pmatrix} -4 \\ 3 \end{pmatrix}$.

State the vector for:
(a) 4 back, 3 down   (b) 4 forward, 3 up   (c) 4 forward, 3 down
(d) 2 back, 5 up   (e) 2 forward, 5 up   (f) 2 back, 5 down.

*4 (a) Repeat question 1, then draw the seven vectors in question 3, including the one in the example.

(b) Draw the vector needed to give your diagram line symmetry in both axes. State the vector as a column matrix. Did you remember the arrows?!

5 Look at your diagram for question 2. Apart from one vector it has line symmetry in both axes. Draw and name the three extra position vectors needed to give the diagram perfect line symmetry in both axes.

6 Repeat question 1, then draw a rectangle 8 units across and 4 units high with its centre at the origin. Draw and name the four position vectors from the origin to the corners of the rectangle.

7 On your diagram for question 6 draw the position vectors $\begin{pmatrix} 1 \\ -2 \end{pmatrix}$ and $\begin{pmatrix} -4 \\ -1 \end{pmatrix}$. Draw and name the position vectors now needed to give your diagram line symmetry in both axes.

---

8 Consider the connection between position vectors and co-ordinates. Why are position vectors so called?

9 Draw a simple pattern or picture on a grid. Define by position vectors the corners of your shape. What problems would you meet in giving your position vectors to a friend and expecting him or her to reproduce your shape exactly? How could you overcome these problems?

B   Shift vectors

Position vectors always start at the origin.

Shift vectors can start anywhere.

In Figure 25:2, both $\overrightarrow{EF}$ and $\overrightarrow{HG}$ are the shift vector $\begin{pmatrix} 4 \\ -4 \end{pmatrix}$ as both are a move of 4 forward and 4 down.

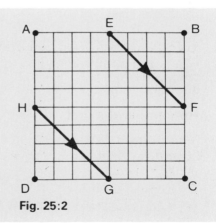

Fig. 25:2

1 Copy Figure 25:2 then draw (with arrows) the following shift vectors.

   (a) $\overrightarrow{DE}$ (b) $\overrightarrow{HE}$ (c) $\overrightarrow{AF}$ (d) $\overrightarrow{GF}$ (e) $\overrightarrow{FD}$ (f) $\overrightarrow{AH}$ (g) $\overrightarrow{CG}$
   (h) $\overrightarrow{FC}$ (i) $\overrightarrow{EA}$

2 In your diagram $\overrightarrow{EF} = \begin{pmatrix} 4 \\ -4 \end{pmatrix}$. Write in a similar way vectors (a) to (i) in question 1.

   Start: $\overrightarrow{DE} = \begin{pmatrix} \\ \end{pmatrix}$; ...

25

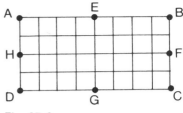

*3 Copy Figure 25:3. Draw the following shift vectors (remembering the arrows).

(a) $\overrightarrow{HB}$ (b) $\overrightarrow{GF}$ (c) $\overrightarrow{BG}$ (d) $\overrightarrow{EG}$

(e) $\overrightarrow{HE}$ (f) $\overrightarrow{GH}$ (g) $\overrightarrow{FB}$ (h) $\overrightarrow{AH}$

(i) $\overrightarrow{FC}$ (j) $\overrightarrow{EA}$

Fig. 25:3

*4 Describe each vector in question 3 using figures. Start: $\overrightarrow{HB} = \begin{pmatrix} 8 \\ 2 \end{pmatrix}$; ...

5 In Figure 25:2 the shift vector $\begin{pmatrix} 4 \\ -4 \end{pmatrix}$ could be $\overrightarrow{EF}$ or $\overrightarrow{HG}$ (if it had to be from one lettered point to another). Using the lettered points give all possible vectors (at least two each time) for:

(a) $\begin{pmatrix} 4 \\ 4 \end{pmatrix}$ (b) $\begin{pmatrix} 8 \\ 4 \end{pmatrix}$ (c) $\begin{pmatrix} -8 \\ -4 \end{pmatrix}$ (d) $\begin{pmatrix} 8 \\ -4 \end{pmatrix}$ (e) $\begin{pmatrix} 8 \\ 0 \end{pmatrix}$ (f) $\begin{pmatrix} 0 \\ -8 \end{pmatrix}$.

6 In Figure 25:4, $\underset{\sim}{a}$ is the shift vector $\begin{pmatrix} 2 \\ -1 \end{pmatrix}$.

$2\underset{\sim}{a}$ is the shift vector $\begin{pmatrix} 4 \\ -2 \end{pmatrix}$. It is in the same direction as $\underset{\sim}{a}$ but twice as long.

$-\frac{1}{2}\underset{\sim}{a}$ is the shift vector $\begin{pmatrix} -1 \\ \frac{1}{2} \end{pmatrix}$. It is opposite in direction to $\underset{\sim}{a}$ and only half as long.

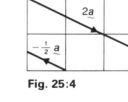

Fig. 25:4

Note that $-\frac{1}{2}\underset{\sim}{a} = -\frac{1}{2}\begin{pmatrix} 2 \\ -1 \end{pmatrix} = \begin{pmatrix} -1 \\ \frac{1}{2} \end{pmatrix}$.

Remember: $-\frac{1}{2} \times 2 = -1$ and $-\frac{1}{2} \times -1 = +\frac{1}{2}$.

Draw $\underset{\sim}{b} = \begin{pmatrix} 3 \\ -2 \end{pmatrix}$. Then draw the following vectors, stating each as a column matrix like $\begin{pmatrix} 3 \\ -2 \end{pmatrix}$.

(a) $2\underset{\sim}{b}$ (b) $-\underset{\sim}{b}$ (c) $-2\underset{\sim}{b}$ (d) $\frac{1}{2}\underset{\sim}{b}$ (e) $-\frac{1}{2}\underset{\sim}{b}$

7 Draw $\underset{\sim}{c} = \begin{pmatrix} -1 \\ -2 \end{pmatrix}$.

Then draw the following vectors and state what each is in terms of $\underset{\sim}{c}$, like $2\underset{\sim}{c}$ and $-\frac{1}{2}\underset{\sim}{c}$.

(a) $\begin{pmatrix} -2 \\ -4 \end{pmatrix}$ (b) $\begin{pmatrix} 1 \\ 2 \end{pmatrix}$ (c) $\begin{pmatrix} 2 \\ 4 \end{pmatrix}$ (d) $\begin{pmatrix} 3 \\ 6 \end{pmatrix}$ (e) $\begin{pmatrix} -\frac{1}{2} \\ -1 \end{pmatrix}$

8 Write a sentence about each of the following vectors, describing how it compares with vector $\underline{a}$.
(a) $-\underline{a}$ (b) $2\underline{a}$ (c) $-2\underline{a}$ (d) $\frac{1}{2}\underline{a}$ (e) $-\frac{1}{2}\underline{a}$ (f) $k\underline{a}$ (g) $-k\underline{a}$

9 Investigate the shift vectors for moves in a game of chess.

C   Translations parallel to the axes

> **A translation is a sliding movement in one direction.**

If the shaded rectangle in Figure 25:5 slides forward to the bottom right-hand corner (from A1B1 to D1E1) it has been **translated** by the shift vector $\begin{pmatrix} 3 \\ 0 \end{pmatrix}$.

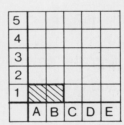

Fig. 25:5

Similarly the shift vector $\begin{pmatrix} -3 \\ 0 \end{pmatrix}$ translates the rectangle back from D1E1 to A1B1.

1 State the shift vector for the translation:
(a) A1B1 to B1C1   (b) A1B1 to A2B2   (c) A1B1 to A4B4
(d) A3B3 to D3E3   (e) B2C2 to B1C1   (f) D5E5 to B5C5
(g) C4D4 to A4B4   (h) A4B4 to A2B2.

2 If the shaded rectangle is moved to E1E2, then the vector $\begin{pmatrix} 0 \\ 3 \end{pmatrix}$ will translate it to E4E5.

State the vector that translates the rectangle from:
(a) E1E2 to E3E4   (b) E1E2 to A1A2   (c) E4E5 to E1E2   (d) E4E5 to A4A5.

.3 Copy Figure 25:6.

Point A, with co-ordinates (2,3), is translated by the vector $\begin{pmatrix} 2 \\ 0 \end{pmatrix}$ to A'.

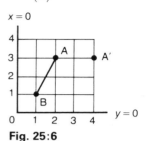

Fig. 25:6

State the co-ordinates of A'.

Apply the same vector to B to give B'.

Join A'B'.

You should have translated the line AB along the grid to A'B'.

A'B' should be the same length as AB and parallel to it.

4 Draw on the grid you drew for question 3 the line A"B" where A" is (2,4) and B" is (1,2).

What vector caused AB to slide to this new position?

5 Translate AB to A'''B''' using shift vector $\begin{pmatrix} -1 \\ 0 \end{pmatrix}$.

State the new co-ordinates of A and B.

6 By writing the co-ordinates of A as the column matrix $\begin{pmatrix} 2 \\ 3 \end{pmatrix}$ we can show by matrix addition why (2,3) moves to (4,3).

$$\begin{pmatrix} 2 \\ 3 \end{pmatrix} + \begin{pmatrix} 2 \\ 0 \end{pmatrix} = \begin{pmatrix} 4 \\ 3 \end{pmatrix}$$

Write similar equations for the effect of $\begin{pmatrix} 2 \\ 0 \end{pmatrix}$ on B, (1,1) and of $\begin{pmatrix} 0 \\ 1 \end{pmatrix}$ and $\begin{pmatrix} -1 \\ 0 \end{pmatrix}$ on A, (2,3) and B, (1,1).

---

7 Investigate the effect of two vectors at right angles.

For instance, $\begin{pmatrix} 3 \\ 0 \end{pmatrix}$ followed by $\begin{pmatrix} 0 \\ -1 \end{pmatrix}$.

Is $\begin{pmatrix} 0 \\ -1 \end{pmatrix}$ followed by $\begin{pmatrix} 3 \\ 0 \end{pmatrix}$ the same as $\begin{pmatrix} 3 \\ 0 \end{pmatrix}$ followed by $\begin{pmatrix} 0 \\ -1 \end{pmatrix}$?

What single vector gives the same result as two vectors?

Find a rule to calculate this vector.

D Translations to slide obliquely

If the shaded rectangle in Figure 25:7 is translated by the vector $\begin{pmatrix} 3 \\ 2 \end{pmatrix}$ it slides to D3E3.

$\begin{pmatrix} 3 \\ 2 \end{pmatrix}$ shifts 3 forward and 2 up.

You can either go along then up, or slide directly from A1B1 to D3E3 at an angle.

Both translations give the same end result, but the journeys are of different lengths.

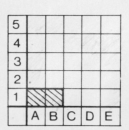

Fig. 25:7

1   State the result of translating the shaded rectangle in Figure 25:7 by:
(a) $\begin{pmatrix} 2 \\ 1 \end{pmatrix}$ (b) $\begin{pmatrix} 1 \\ 4 \end{pmatrix}$ (c) $\begin{pmatrix} 2 \\ 2 \end{pmatrix}$ (d) $\begin{pmatrix} 3 \\ 1 \end{pmatrix}$ (e) $\begin{pmatrix} 2 \\ 3 \end{pmatrix}$.

2   State the result of translating from E1E2 by:
(a) $\begin{pmatrix} -1 \\ 2 \end{pmatrix}$ (b) $\begin{pmatrix} -4 \\ 3 \end{pmatrix}$ (c) $\begin{pmatrix} -2 \\ 2 \end{pmatrix}$.

3   State the vector that gives the translation:
(a) A2B2 to C3D3   (b) A5B5 to C4D4   (c) E3E4 to A2A3   (d) D4E4 to A1B1.

4   Copy the shape in Figure 25:8 exactly on plain paper, leaving about 6 cm to its right and about 6 cm below it.

Starting each part from the original position, draw the shape in its new position after a translation of:

Fig. 25:8

(a) 3 cm to the right   (b) 3 cm downwards
(c) 3 cm downwards at an angle of 45° to the vertical. (Be very careful. Do not jump to conclusions! Translate!)

5   Repeat question 4 but each time go on from the *new* position.

6   When a figure is reflected it stays the same shape and size but is reversed left to right in a vertical mirror. Investigate the effect of translation on a shape. Try to write a description of what changes and what stays the same.

Example   10 tins of food a week are required to feed 3 cats. How many tins would be required for 4 cats?

Ratio Method
The number of cats has increased in the ratio 4:3.
The number of tins must increase in the same ratio.
To increase in the ratio 4:3, multiply by $\frac{4}{3}$.
Answer: $10 \times \frac{4}{3} = 13\frac{1}{3}$ tins.

Unitary ('one') Method
3 cats require 10 tins
1 cat requires $\frac{10}{3}$ tins
4 cats will require $4 \times \frac{10}{3} = 13\frac{1}{3}$ tins.

Questions for Discussion

(a) Three eggs cost 15p. What do eight eggs cost?

(b) Three packets weigh 5 kg. What will seven of the same packets weigh?

(c) A spring increases by 36 mm with a 7.2 kg load. What is the increase with a 9.2 kg load?

(d) Four men on a raft have enough food for 21 days. If three more survivors are picked up, how long will the food last at the same rate?

(e) £14 will feed two cats for 12 weeks. For how long will £21 feed them? If a stray joins the two cats, for how long will the £14 feed them?

1   A bus travels 100 km in 4 hours. How far would it travel in 3 hours?

2   A man pays the same tax each week. He pays £500 in 8 weeks. How much will he pay in 10 weeks?

3   Six exercise books cost £1. What will fifteen exercise books cost?

4   Eight cubic metres of a substance weigh 148 kg. What will 3 m³ of the substance weigh?

*5 Write what is needed to complete the following.

(a) A train with 3 carriages can seat 180 people.
A train with 4 carriages can seat . . .

(b) Three kilograms of flour cost 96 pence.
Four kilograms of flour cost . . .

(c) Two pints of peas sow 5 lines.
Five pints of peas sow . . .

(d) A 50 ml bottle of ink will fill a pen 30 times.
A 125 ml bottle of ink will fill a pen . . .

(e) Seven men can paint a school in 4 days.
Eight men can paint the school in . . .

*6 A ferry charges lorries by the number of wheels they have. An eight-wheeler costs £20. What will a ten-wheeler cost?

7 With two pumps working it takes 30 hours to empty an oil-tanker. How long will it take with five pumps working?

8 Find the cost of eight cakes if twelve cost £4.08.

9 A machine can lay 4 metres of road in 11 seconds. How long will it take to lay 1 km: (a) in seconds   (b) in minutes to the nearest minute?

10 450 ml of Bell's gloss paint will cover approximately 27 m^2.

(a) How much paint is needed for 100 m^2 in ml to the nearest ml?

(b) How many 450 ml tins will be needed?

11 I can type about 27 words a minute. It takes me about 20 minutes to type one page. The school secretary takes about 9 minutes to type one page. About how many words a minute does she type?

12 A field of grass lasts 17 cows about twelve days. About how many days will it last 20 cows?

13 If 100 shares in a company cost £105, how many can I buy for £42?

14 At 40 km/h I can reach Bristol in 65 minutes. What speed must I average to reach Bristol in not more than 60 minutes? (Answer to be integral.)

15 (a) Increase 27 metres in the ratio 16:9.

(b) Decrease a speed of 45 km/h in the ratio 8:15.

(c) Increase £120 in the ratio 5:4.

(d) Decrease 196 in the ratio 3:8.

16 If three cats fight twice a day how often will nine cats fight?

17 Four potatoes take $1\frac{1}{2}$ hours to roast. For how long should I roast ten potatoes?

18 Are the following statements true?

(a) Henry VIII had six wives therefore Henry IV had three wives.

(b) In 1 hour I catch 5 fish so in 3 hours I will catch 15 fish.

(c) If two fighting cats keep six people awake then six fighting cats will keep eighteen people awake.

(d) If a girl of ten eats four meals a day then a lady of thirty eats twelve meals a day.

Make up some more incorrect uses of proportion.

Project

Constructing prisms

A prism is a solid with all parallel cross-sections through it having an identical shape.

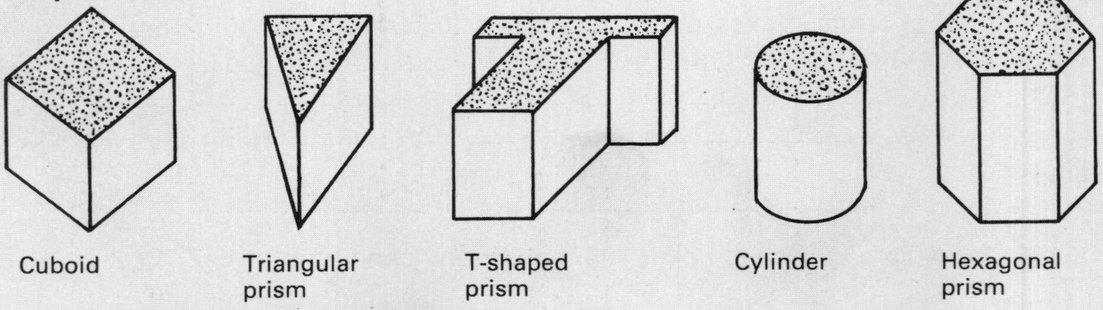

Cuboid   Triangular prism   T-shaped prism   Cylinder   Hexagonal prism

Fig. P2:1   Some prisms

1 Draw the net shown in Figure P2:2 on 1 cm-squared paper. Cut it out and form a cuboid.

How many centimetre cubes could you fit inside it?

What is the volume of the cuboid? How could you calculate the answer?

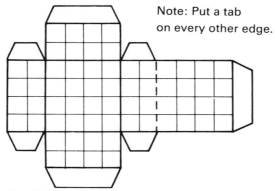

Note: Put a tab
on every other edge.

Fig. P2:2

2 Make a model of the cuboid drawn in Figure P2:3.

How many cm cubes could you fit inside it?

What is its volume?

Fig. P2:3

3 Copy the nets in Figure P2:4a–c on 1 cm-squared paper, adding tabs for glueing. Remember 'Tab on every other edge'.

Cut out the nets and form the prisms.

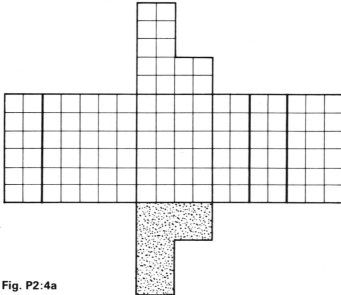

Fig. P2:4a

137

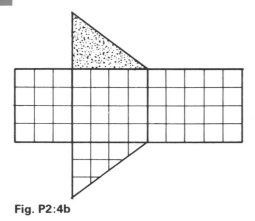

Fig. P2:4b

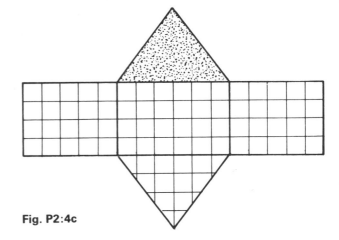

Fig. P2:4c

4 Isometric paper can be used to draw shapes in 3D (three dimensions). Study Figure P2:5 before using isometric paper to draw the letters L, E, F and H in a similar style.
(Hint: Vertical lines always remain vertical.)

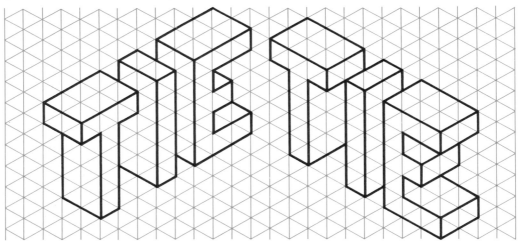

Fig. P2:5

5 Using squared paper, draw nets of the letters you drew for question 4.

6 Using isometric paper, draw your name in 3D letters.

A Foreign Exchange

TOURIST RATES (JULY 1989)

Country	Currency	Rate to £1
Austria	Schilling	OS 22.60
Belgium	Franc	FB 65.90
Denmark	Kroner	DKr 12.55
France	Franc	FF 10.55
West Germany	Deutschmark	DM 3.22
Spain	Peseta	Pta 201.00
Switzerland	Franc	Fs 2.77
U.S.A.	Dollar	$ 1.74

Fig. 27:1

1 Example £1 = DKr12.55 so £15 = 15 × DKr12.55 = DKr188.25

Change the following for use in the given country.
(a) £10 for Austria   (b) £10 for Spain   (c) £40 for France
(d) £100 for U.S.A.   (e) £15 for Belgium   (f) £35 for Switzerland

*2 Change into each of the currencies in the table at the start of the exercise:
(a) £70   (b) £25.

You may use a calculator in the following questions.

3 Change into Sterling (£'s):
(a) OS 232   (b) FB 462   (c) FF 85.50   (d) $ 46.20   (e) Fs 152.40
(f) DKr 832   (g) DM 196.80   (h) FB 2970.

---

4 Change 250 units of each currency in the table into Sterling.

5 Draw a graph to convert up to £10 (in multiples of 10p) into Deutschmarks (in multiples of 50 pfennigs).

Note: 100 pfennigs = 1 Deutschmark.

B   Timetables

Example   Using 24-hour-clock time find the time 10h 47 min after 1426.

14h 26 min	**Notes**	6 + 7 = 13; 3, carry 1.

    14 h 26 min   **Notes** 6 + 7 = 13; 3, carry 1.
+ 10 h 47 min   4 + 2 + carry 1 = 7, making 73 min.
    25 h 13 min → *Answer* 0113. 73 min = 1 h 13 min.

Example   How long is it from 0357 to 1951?

   19 h 51 min   18 h 111 min
− 03 h 57 min →   − 03 h   57 min
              Answer 15 h   54 min

Note 57 min cannot be taken from 51 min, so change
19 h 51 min to 18 h 111 min.

1 Find the time:
(a) 4 h 29 min after 2116   (b) 5 h 56 min after 2312   (c) 6 h 42 min after 2037
(d) 1 h 15 min after 2246.

2 How long is it from:
(a) 1557 to 1952   (b) 0859 to 1742   (c) 1157 to 1236   (d) 0716 to 1225
(e) 0154 to 0346?

*3 Find the time:
(a) 3 h 46 min after 1203   (b) 6 h 47 min after 1523   (c) 9 h 59 min after 1303
(d) 12 h 16 min after 1531   (e) 18 h 53 min after 1625.

*4 How long is it from:
(a) 0642 to 0936   (b) 0532 to 1023   (c) 1509 to 1806   (d) 1632 to 1747
(e) 1756 to 2153?

5 Figure 27:2 shows a bus timetable.

(a) What is the time interval between each bus leaving Burnham-on-Sea?

(b) How long does each bus take from Burnham-on-Sea to Taunton?

(c) For how long does each bus stop at Bridgwater?

Burnham-on-Sea *dep.*	0720	0805	0820	0905	0935	1035	1135	1235
Bridgwater *arr.*	0758	0843	0858	0943	1013	1113	1213	1313
Bridgwater *dep.*	0807	0848	0902	0948	1018	1118	1218	1318
Taunton *arr.*	0847	0928	0942	1028	1058	1158	1258	1358

Fig. 27:2

		A ☕	B ✗☕	C ☕	D ☕	E ✗☕	F ☕	G ✗☕	H ☕	I SX
Departs	**Birmingham New Street**	1215	1315	1420	1515	1620	1715	1810	1915	2137
Arrives	Cheltenham Spa		1357	1516	1557	1657	1758	1853	1958	2241
	Gloucester				1611		1812			2300
	Bristol Parkway			1556	1648		1849	1936	2036	
	Bristol Temple Meads	1351	1452	1611	1703	1800	1904	1951	**2051**	2355
	Weston-Super-Mare		1519	1647	1730					
	Taunton	1438	1549	1724	1803	1854	1957	2050		
	Exeter St David	**1512**	**1624**	**1812**	**1836**	**1929**	**2037**	**2142**		

NOTES

☕ Buffet service of drinks and cold snacks ⎫ For whole or part of
✗ Restaurant service according to time of day ⎬ the journey
SX Saturday excepted

Fig. 27:3

6 Figure 27:3 shows a rail timetable.

(a) What do the blank spaces on the timetable mean?

(b) At which station do all the trains shown stop?

(c) I arrive at Birmingham New Street station at 4.00 p.m. How long should I have to wait for a train to Gloucester?

(d) Which trains from Birmingham do not stop at Gloucester? (Answer by letters A to I.)

(e) Which two trains go no further than Bristol?

(f) Which trains provide a restaurant-car?

7 How long does each train take from Birmingham to:
(a) Bristol Temple Meads   (b) Exeter St David?

8 Birmingham is 280 km from Exeter. Find the average speed of each train.

9 Make a display showing some train or bus routes on a map.

C Taking a ferry

TARIFF — ALL FARES SINGLE JOURNEY ONLY

Vehicle Rates

Length not exceeding	Standard	Summer Season	Summer Weekend
3.80 m	£17	£21	£24
4.30 m	£23	£28	£32
4.70 m	£30	£36	£41
over 4.70 m	£35	£42	£49
Motor cycles	£6	£7	£8
Bicycles (Belg.)	£3	£3	£3
(France)	Free	Free	Free
Caravans, each 0.30 m or part	£1.50	£2	£2.50

Fig. 27:4

Motorists' Fares

Adults	£10
Child 4–13	£5
Pensioner	£7
Child under 4	Free

Tariff Period

Standard	Jan/June Sept/Dec
Summer Season	Sun–Thurs July/Aug
Summer Weekend	Fri–Sat July/Aug

1 What is the Summer Season cost for a car of length:
(a) 4.20 m   (b) 4.40 m?

2 What is the cost of single tickets for:
(a) 2 adults   (b) a child of twelve   (c) a fourteen-year old
(d) two pensioners   (e) two adults, a child of eleven and a child of three?

3 What is the Summer Weekend cost for a caravan of length:
(a) 3 m   (b) 4.20 m   (c) 2.90 m   (d) 4.30 m?

4 Copy and complete the reservation shown in Figure 27:5.

NAME: *James Tripper*		OUT: *Standard*		RETURN: *Summer season*	
Adults	*2*	£ *20*	*00*	£	
Children 4–13	*1*	£		£	
Pensioners	*1*	£		£	
Children under 4	*1*	Free		Free	
Car length	*4.40 m*	£		£	
Motorcycles	✗	£		£	
Bicycles	✗	£		£	GRAND TOTAL
Caravan length	*4.80 m*	£		£	
TOTAL COSTS		£		£	£ :

Fig. 27:5

5 Make out a reservation for 2 adults, 3 children aged 14, 10 and 8, a car (3.85 m long) and a caravan (3.10 m long).

The outward journey is to be at Standard prices and the return journey at Summer Weekend prices.

6 If all tariff charges increase by 10% write out the new tariff.

7 Make a collection of brochures showing prices for journeys.

28 Angles: parallel lines

A Adjacent and vertically opposite angles

In Figure 28:1

$a + b = 180°$ (**Adjacent** angles on a straight line.)

$a = c$ (**Vertically opposite** angles.)

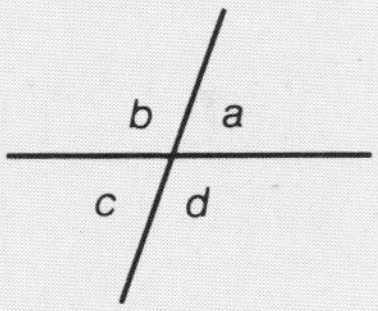

Fig. 28:1

1 Copy Figure 28:1 and the statements about it. Then write similar statements about:

(a) the other three pairs of adjacent angles in Figure 28:1

(b) the other pair of vertically opposite angles in Figure 28:1.

2 Examples

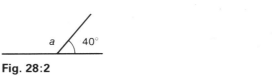

Fig. 28:2

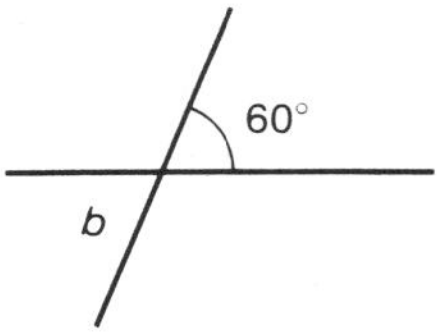

Fig. 28:3

In Figure 28:2, $a = 140°$ (Adjacent angles on a straight line.)

In Figure 28:3, $b = 60°$ (Vertically opposite angles.)

Calculate, with a reason in brackets as in the examples, the value of each letter in Figure 28:4.

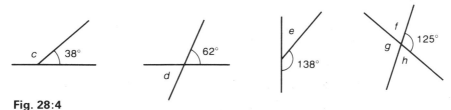

Fig. 28:4

***3** Calculate, with reasons, the value of *m*, *n*, *p*, *q* and *s* in Figure 28:5.

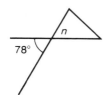
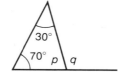

Fig. 28:5

*4   In Figure 28:6 the triangle is equilateral. Copy the diagram, but larger, and write in the sizes of all twelve angles.

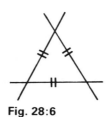

5   In Figure 28:7 the triangle is isosceles. Copy the diagram, but larger, and write in the sizes of the other eleven angles.

Fig. 28:6

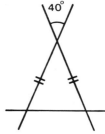

Fig. 28:7

6   (a) If $a + 70° = 180°$ and $c + 70° = 180°$ how many degrees are a and c?

   (b) If $a + 100° = 180°$ and $c + 100° = 180°$ how many degrees are a and c?

   (c) If $a + b = 180°$ and $c + b = 180°$ what can you say about a and c?

   (d) We can prove that the vertically opposite angles a and c in Figure 28:8 are equal. Copy the figure and the proof. Make sure that you understand it.

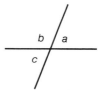

Note that the sign ∴ means 'therefore'.

Fig. 28:8

Proof

$a + b = 180°$ (Adjacent angles on a straight line.)

$c + b = 180°$ (Adjacent angles on a straight line.)

∴ $a = c$ (Both, added to b, equal 180°.)

7   If, in Figure 28:8, $a = 40°$ and $c = 50°$, what would you know about at least one of the two lines?

8   Copy Figure 28:9, then copy and complete:

   $... + a = 180°$ (Adjacent ...)

   $... + ... + a = 180°$ (Angle sum of triangle)

   ∴ $e = b + c$ (Both + ... = ...)

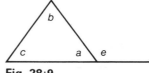

Fig. 28:9

B Parallel line angles

In Figure 28:10 $a = f$ (**Corresponding** angles.)

$d = e$ (**Alternate** angles.)

$d + f = 180°$ (**Allied** angles.)

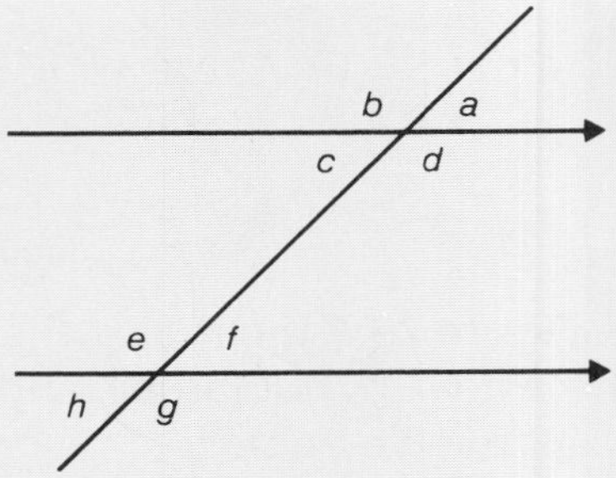

Fig. 28:10

1   Write similar statements to those above for:

(a) the other three pairs of corresponding angles in Figure 28:10

(b) the other pair of alternate angles in Figure 28:10

(c) the other pair of allied angles in Figure 28:10.

2   State, with a reason in brackets, the value of each lettered angle in Figure 28:11.

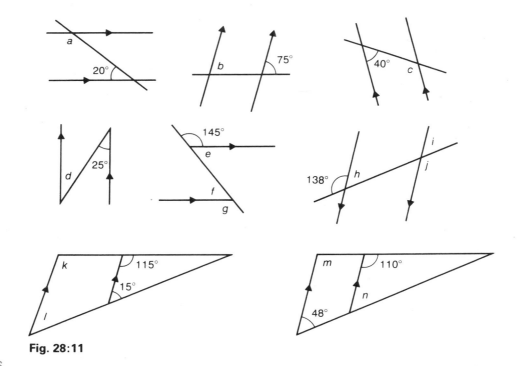

Fig. 28:11

3 Using the kinds of angles you have learnt about, and the facts you know about triangles and quadrilaterals, find the value of each lettered angle in alphabetical order.

Notes (i) Copy each diagram about twice as big, writing in the sizes of the angles as you find them.

(ii) List your answers with reasons, e.g. $h = 38°$ (equal angles in isosceles triangles); $i = 62°$ (opposite angles of rhombus).

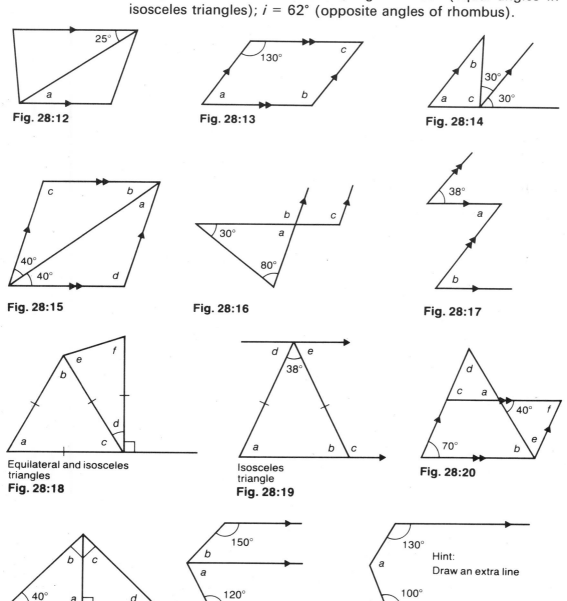

Fig. 28:12

Fig. 28:13

Fig. 28:14

Fig. 28:15

Fig. 28:16

Fig. 28:17

Equilateral and isosceles triangles
Fig. 28:18

Isosceles triangle
Fig. 28:19

Fig. 28:20

Fig. 28:21

Fig. 28:22

Hint:
Draw an extra line

Fig. 28:23

Project

Decision trees

Decision trees can be used to identify objects. This example can be used to identify a quadrilateral. As usual in a flow-chart, all questions must have a Yes/No answer.

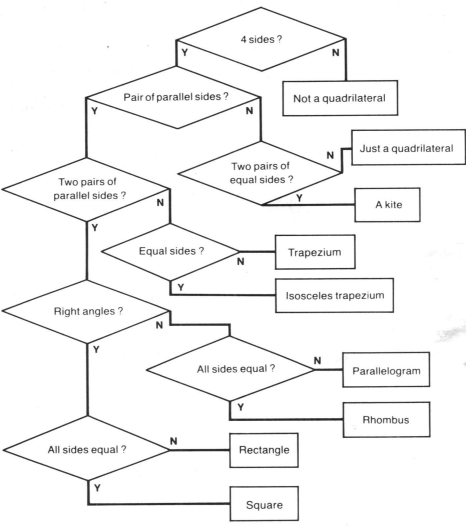

Fig. P3:1

Develop your own decision trees. Here are some ideas to start you off:

- Identify a triangle (Scalene/Isosceles/Equilateral + Acute/Right/Obtuse).
- Identify a spring flower from Daffodil/Tulip/Aconite/Forsythia/Polyanthus/Crocus.
- Identify a coin if you were blind.

A   Percentages involving money

Fig. 29:1

1   A shop expects about 5% of the items it sells to be returned as faulty. How many faulty items does it expect for every hundred sold?

2   What percentage is a Hire Purchase interest rate of 18p in the pound?

3   If a quarter of the stock in a sale is damaged, what percentage of the stock is *not* damaged?

4   What is:
(a) 1% of £1   (b) 20% of £1   (c) 20% of £20   (d) 15% of £1   (e) 15% of £4
(f) 15% of £10?

5   Mosha has to change the price tickets in the shop window shown in Figure 29:1 to the sale prices. Use your answers to question 4 to find what prices he should write.

6   What fraction, as simply as possible, is:
(a) 20%   (b) 15%   (c) 27%?

7   Maria scores 17 out of 25 in a test. What percentage score is this?

8 Example In Figure 29:2, the Police are given 9% of the £200 charge paid.
9% of £200 = £18.

What amounts did the householder pay for the other services?

COMMUNITY CHARGE £200

POLICE 9%

FIRE 5%

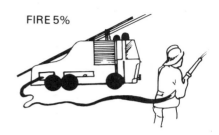

HIGHWAYS 12%

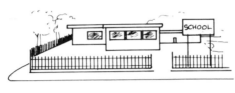

Fig. 29:2

EDUCATION 60%

*9 Find:
(a) 5% of £1   (b) 5% of £3   (c) 9% of £1   (d) 9% of £8   (e) 14% of £1
(f) 14% of £9   (g) 8% of £10   (h) 2% of £15.

*10 In the following table, study the completed columns for £8 and £6, then find what
should be written in sections (a) to (h).

Cost Price	£8	£6	£5	£9	£7	£12
Profit/Loss %	10% profit	7% loss	7% profit	15% profit	6% loss	8% loss
Profit/Loss	80p profit	42p loss	(a)	(c)	(e)	(g)
Selling Price	£8.80	£5.58	(b)	(d)	(f)	(h)

11 Another householder in the same area as the one in question 8 paid £140.
How much did he pay towards each of the services?

12 Arthur buys and sells pictures. He made 100% profit when he sold for £5000 a picture
which cost him £2500.

What is his percentage profit on a picture sold for £1000 if he paid £250 for it?

13 Gwyneth receives a 17% increase in her pay when she is promoted. What is her new pay if she *was* earning £600?

14 Simon sells his bicycle at a loss of 20%. He paid £96 for it. What did he receive when he sold it?

15 Example $27\frac{1}{2}\%$ → $\dfrac{27\frac{1}{2}}{100}$ → $\dfrac{55}{200}$ → $\dfrac{11}{40}$

> **Note**   The awkward $\frac{1}{2}$ was removed by multiplying the top and bottom of $\dfrac{27\frac{1}{2}}{100}$ by 2.

Write as a simplified fraction:
(a) $12\frac{1}{2}\%$ (b) $7\frac{1}{2}\%$ (c) $1\frac{1}{4}\%$ (multiply top and bottom by 4)
(d) $3\frac{3}{4}\%$ ($4 \times \frac{1}{4} = 1$, so $4 \times \frac{3}{4} = 3$)   (e) $33\frac{1}{3}\%$ (f) $6\frac{3}{4}\%$.

You may use a calculator in the following questions.

16 Find correct to the nearest penny:
(a) $2\frac{1}{2}\%$ of £5.34   (b) $6\frac{1}{4}\%$ of £83.16

17 A shop wishes to make a profit of $62\frac{1}{2}\%$ on its cost prices.

Find to the nearest penny the selling price before and after 15% VAT is added for an article of cost price:
(a) £83.63   (b) £2500.10

---

18 The total cost price of an article is made up of 5% materials, 65% labour and 30% overheads.

(a) If the materials for one article cost 8p what would be:
 (i) the labour cost (Hint: $5 \times 13 = 65$)
 (ii) the overheads cost?

(b) What is the total cost price of one article?

(c) At what price must the article be sold to make 20% profit?

(d) A different article cost £4 to make. Find the cost of the materials, labour and overheads if the percentages are the same as for the first article.

19 Investigate the effect on £100 of a 10% increase followed by a 10% decrease.

B Percentages of amounts

Example Find 35% of 45.

35% means $\frac{35}{100}$; 'of' means multiply.

So 35% of 45 $\rightarrow \frac{35}{100} \times 45 \rightarrow \frac{^7 35 \times 45^9}{_{4}20 \; 100} = \frac{63}{4} = 15\frac{3}{4}$.

1 Find:
(a) 6% of 50   (b) 20% of 35   (c) 14% of 225   (d) 9% of 125.

*2 Find:
(a) 7% of 140   (b) 6% of 120   (c) 15% of 250   (d) 90% of 70
(e) 12% of 125   (f) 9% of 225.

*3 Write:
(a) 2 m in cm   (b) 20 m in cm   (c) 3 kg in g   (d) 3 litres in ml
(e) 4 km in m   (f) 7 tonnes in kg.

4 Find:

(a) 28% of 1 m in cm (Hint: First write 1 m in cm.)

(b) 24% of 1 kg in g (Hint: First write 1 kg in g.)

(c) 7% of 5 km in m

(d) 12% of 15 litres in ml

(e) 15% of 7 tonnes in kg.

5

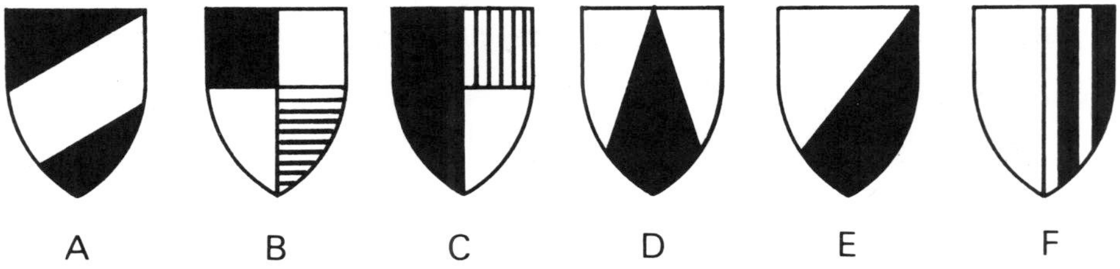

A   B   C   D   E   F
Fig. 29:3

All 960 pupils in a school vote for six different school badge designs as shown in Figure 29:3. The result is shown in the pie-chart of Figure 29:4. Calculate how many pupils voted for each design.

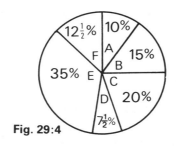

Fig. 29:4

6 A class of 32 pupils filled in a questionnaire to show their favourite pastime.

The result was: Sport 50%; Reading 25%; Fishing $12\frac{1}{2}$%; Walking $6\frac{1}{4}$%.

(a) How many pupils chose each pastime?
(b) What percentage of the class did *not* choose one of these pastimes?
(c) Illustrate the result.

---

7 In 1981 Roy and Sue earned the same salary. In 1982 Roy had a 6% rise and Sue had an 8% rise. In 1983 Roy had an 8% rise and Sue had a 6% rise. Compare their pay after both rises.

8 A gift cost £20 inclusive of 15% VAT. What did it cost before VAT was added? Check your answer by adding the VAT back on.

9 Collect examples of percentages from newspapers. Discuss them with your class.

10 **Using your calculator**

The %̲ key does not have the same effect on all calculators. Most calculators fall into one of two categories, but consult your handbook if you meet problems.

To find out if your calculator is type A or type B, key in 5 %̲ . Type A calculators now display 5 or 0; type B calculators now display 0.05.

Try the following to find 35% of £200 (Answer £70).

Type A 200 ×̲ 35 %̲

Type B 200 ×̲ 35 %̲ =̲ **OR** 35 %̲ ×̲ 200 =̲

Try the following to add 15% VAT to £200 (Answer £230).

Type A 200 +̲ 15 %̲ **OR** 200 ×̲ 15 %̲ =̲ +̲

Type B 200 +̲ 15 %̲ =̲

30 Metric system: problems

A Length

1000 millimetres	= 1 metre	1000 mm	= 1 m
100 centimetres	= 1 metre	100 cm	= 1 m
10 decimetres	= 1 metre	10 dm	= 1 m
10 metres	= 1 decametre	10 m	= 1 dam
100 metres	= 1 hectametre	100 m	= 1 hm
1000 metres	= 1 kilometre	1000 m	= 1 km

1 Change to centimetres:
(a) 1 m (b) 8 m (c) 2.5 m (d) 3.75 m (e) 4.06 m.

2 How many millimetres long is a line of length:
(a) 1 cm (b) 6 cm (c) 3.8 cm?

3 How many metres make:
(a) 1 km (b) 0.5 km?

4 Write as a decimal of a cm:
(a) 1 cm 4 mm (b) 25 mm (c) 6 mm.

5 Write as a decimal of a metre:
(a) 1 m 88 cm (b) 162 cm (c) 25 cm (d) 1 cm.

***6**

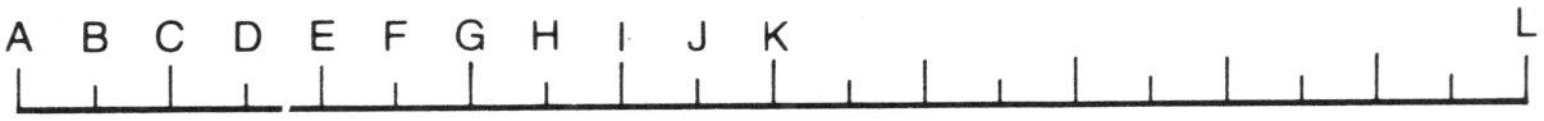
A B C D E F G H I J K L

Fig. 30:1

In Figure 30:1

(a) Measure from A to L in cm.

(b) Measure from A to L in mm.

(c) *AC = 1 cm = 10 mm.* Write similar statements about AG, DH, KL, and GL.

(d) *AD = $1\frac{1}{2}$ cm = 1.5 cm = 15 mm.* Write similar statements about AH, DI, JL, and HL.

*7 In Figure 30:2 check that AB is 2.2 cm or 22 mm long.

Write the other lengths in both cm and mm.

A————————B   C——————D   E————————————F   G————————————H
Fig. 30:2

*8 Write as a decimal of a cm:
(a) 4 cm 3 mm   (b) 38 mm   (c) 9 mm   (d) 6 mm.

*9 Write in centimetres:
(a) 0.57 m   (b) 0.48 m   (c) 3.75 m   (d) 5.1 m   (e) 2.06 m.

*10 Write as a decimal of a metre:
(a) 3 m 46 cm   (b) 195 cm   (c) 12 cm   (d) 3 cm   (e) 201 cm.

*11 A kilometre is 1000 metres. Copy and complete:
(a) $\frac{1}{2}$ km = 0.5 km = ... m   (b) $\frac{1}{4}$ km = 0.25 km = ... m   (c) $\frac{3}{4}$ km = ... km = ... m.

12 Write in mm:
(a) 5 m   (b) 5.6 m   (c) 3.75 m   (d) 0.652 m   (e) 4.08 m   (f) 0.01 m
(g) 0.007 m   (h) 0.1015 m.

13

A   2.98 m   3.12 m   5.08 m   15.7 m   **B**
Fig. 30:3

(a) Write the length of each vehicle in centimetres.

(b) If there is 1 metre between each vehicle how far would it be from A to B?

(c) How many centimetres longer is the minibus than:
(i) the car   (ii) the Landrover?

(d) How much longer is the lorry than each other vehicle, in metres?

14 In Figure 30:4:

(a) Measure each horizontal line in:
(i) mm   (ii) cm   (iii) m.

(b) Draw two similar lines of length 0.045 m.

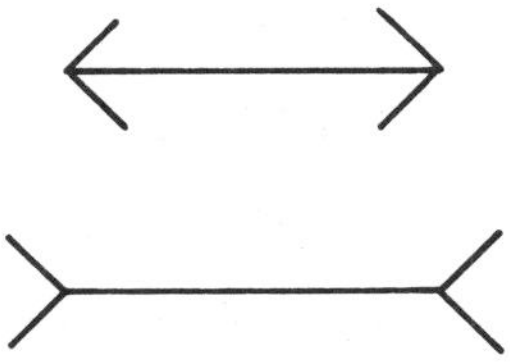

Fig. 30:4

15 Diagrams will help you to answer this question.

Jane, Helen and Paul all live along the same straight road. Jane lives $\frac{1}{2}$ km from Helen and Helen lives $\frac{1}{4}$ km from Paul.

(a) How far from Paul does Jane live? (Two possible answers.)

(b) If Helen visits Paul, then goes back home, then visits Jane and finally returns home again, how many metres does she travel?

(c) Paul lives 0.75 km from school, which is nearer than Helen and Jane. The school is on the same straight road. How far from it does Jane live?

16 By accurate drawing and calculation find the area of an equilateral triangle of side 2.5 cm.

B Weight (mass)

All objects have **mass**. An object has **weight** if a force such as the attraction of the earth (gravity) acts on its mass.

The basic metric unit of mass is the kilogram (kg), which is 1000 grams (g). One milligram (mg) = $\frac{1}{1000}$ g. One tonne = 1000 kg.

On earth objects with the same mass have the same weight. To measure the mass of an object we 'weigh' it (we are measuring the force of gravity on it). Therefore in everyday language 'weight' is often used instead of 'mass': an object with a mass of x kilograms is said to have a weight of x kilograms.

1 How many grams in:
(a) 3 kg (b) 0.5 kg (c) 0.05 kg (d) 0.005 kg?

2 Write in kilograms:
(a) 1200 g (b) 2315 g (c) 360 g (d) 36 g (e) 3 g.

3 Copy and complete the table.

mg				750	1200	2500
g	1	0.5	0.25			

*4 Copy and complete the table:

g	2000	2500	250	100			
kg					0.2	0.6	0.35

5 For the packets shown in Figure 30:5 find the total weight in kilograms of:

(a) 2 pkts of sugar and 1 pkt of butter

(b) 3 pkts of butter and 2 pkts of flour

(c) 2 pkts of detergent and 2 pkts of currants

(d) 3 pkts of flour and 2 pkts of currants

(e) 1 pkt of flour and 3 pkts of detergent

(f) 3 pkts of butter, 2 pkts of detergent and 1 pkt of currants

(g) 3 pkts of flour, 4 pkts of currants and 1 pkt of sage stuffing

(h) 1 pkt of detergent, 1 pkt of sage stuffing, 1 pkt of flour and 3 pkts of butter.

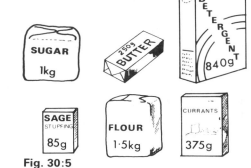

Fig. 30:5

6 Each of the commodities in Figure 30:5 comes to the shop in boxes containing twenty-five packets.

Find the weight of:

(a) each box, in kg

(b) one lorry-load containing ten boxes of each of the six commodities, in tonnes.

7 A recipe for a Victoria Sandwich requires:
100 g butter, 100 g sugar, 100 g flour, 2 eggs.

I buy 1 packet each of butter, sugar and flour to make this cake.

The packets are as shown in Figure 30:5. How many grams of each will be left after I have made the cake?

8 I put about 170 g of detergent into my washing-machine for each wash. About how many washes from the packet in Figure 30:5?

9 Cook has to make twenty Victoria Sandwiches (see question 7). How many packets of each commodity must he buy?

10 You have to weigh any object to the nearest 50 g using the scales shown in Figure 30:6. Show that you can do this for up to 650 g using only a 50 g, a 150 g, and a 450 g weight. Set your answer out in a table.

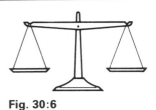

Fig. 30:6

11 If you continue the sequence of question 10, what is the largest possible weight to follow the 450 g weight?

12 Make a weighing machine like the one in Figure 30:7 using an elastic band (or a spring), a paper-clip and scraps of card. Calibrate your scale using known weights. Your Science Department may be able to help you.

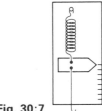

Fig. 30:7

C Capacity

Capacity is used for liquid measurements.

The basic unit is the litre.

The prefixes deca, hecta and kilo are not commonly used in measures of capacity.

1 millilitre (1 ml) is the same as 1 cubic centimetre (1 cm^3).

1 Write in litres:
(a) 1500 ml   (b) 500 ml   (c) 50 ml.

2 Find in ml:
(a) 1.6 litres + 750 ml   (b) 2 litres − 1.75 litres   (c) 0.25 litres × 10.

*3 The scale in Figure 30:8 shows by a moving arrow how many litres of paraffin there are in my oil-heater.

(a) How many litres does the heater hold when full?

(b) How many ml is each division?

(c) What does the arrow show is in the heater now? Answer both in litres and in millilitres.

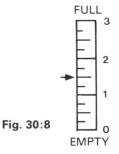

Fig. 30:8

*4 How many litres does each scale read in Figure 30:9?

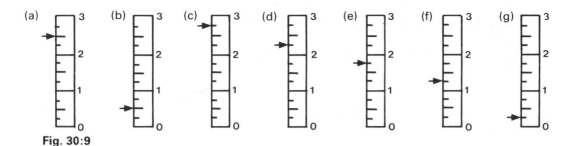

Fig. 30:9

5 Draw neat, accurate scales like those in Figure 30:9 to show:
(a) 2.25 litres   (b) 500 ml   (c) $\frac{2}{3}$ of a full tank   (d) $\frac{3}{4}$ of a full tank.

6 I have to take two 5 ml spoons of medicine three times a day. (Uggh!) How many days will a 0.15 litre bottle last? (Too long!)

7 A soup recipe requires 125 ml of milk per person.

For how many people can I make soup from 1 litre of milk?

8 A swimming pool has a volume of 1500 m³. Remember that 1 m³ = 1000 litres.

(a) What is the capacity of the pool in litres?

(b) If sodium hypochlorate has to be added at 1 part to 30 000 parts of water, how many litres of chemical must be added to a freshly filled pool?

9 A litre of water has a mass of 1 kg.

A litre of mercury has a mass of 13.6 kg.

(a) Calculate the mass of 1 ml of each.

(b) Calculate the mass of 5.6 ml of mercury.

(c) How much heavier is 7.8 ml of mercury than 7.8 ml of water?

10 (a) 2.6 litres + 250 ml   (b) 3.8 litres + 490 ml   (c) 6.5 litres + 160 ml
(d) 5 litres − 250 ml   (e) 4 litres − 1.15 litres   (f) 450 ml × 8 (in litres)

11 A paint firm wishes to make a cylindrical one-litre tin whose diameter is the same as its height. Make a model of this tin and check its volume.

D   Mixed problems

> **Learn**   1000 metres = 1 kilometre
>
> 1000 kilograms = 1 tonne
>
> 1000 litres = 1 cubic metre

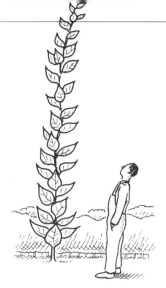

1   A plant 6.5 cm high on Sunday grows 4 mm a day.

How high is it:
(a) each day that week, in cm
(b) in 30 days time, in cm
(c) in 365 days, in metres?

Fig. 30:10

2   A bucket weighs 500 g. What is its total weight when it contains 7.5 kg of sand?

3   When full of sand a 500 g bucket weighs 10.5 kg. How much does the sand weigh?

4   How many times can a bucket be filled from a tonne load of sand, using the bucket in question 3?

5   When making mortar, 4 kg of sand are mixed with 1 kg of cement. How many kg of cement would be needed for a tonne of sand?

6   A cat eats 90 g of food a day. How many 210 g tins of food are needed per week?

7   How many kg of food would a cat eat in 365 days at the rate given in question 6?

8   One tablet of Verve contains 10 mg Vitamin B6 and 188 mg Yeast. How many grams of each in 100 tablets?

9   (a) How many cm is it round the domino drawn in Figure 30:11?

   (b) Eight of the dominoes are laid end to end. How many cm do they reach?

   (c) The box to hold the dominoes has seven layers of four as shown in Figure 30:12. What is the length, width and depth of the box if a domino is 6 mm thick? Answer in centimetres.

5·6 cm

2·8 cm

Fig. 30:11

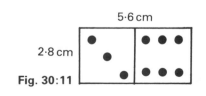

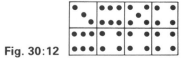

Fig. 30:12

10 A room is 5.3 m long, 4.6 m wide and 3.2 m high. Remember that the area of a rectangle is length × width.

Find:

(a) the floor area in m^2

(b) the total area of all four walls in m^2

(c) the cost of wall-to-wall carpeting at £18.50 per m^2, to the nearest £1.

11 As 8 km is about 5 miles, how many miles is 112 km?

---

12 A weed-killer can either be 'watered' or sprayed onto a lawn.

When watered, 27 ml are to be mixed with 9 litres of water to cover 15 m^2.

When sprayed, 54 ml are to be mixed with 9 litres of water to cover 100 m^2.

The ratio of chemical to water for watering is worked out as follows:
27 ml:9 litres = 27:9000 = 3:1000; giving 3 parts in a thousand.

(a) In the same way, work out the ratio of chemical to water for spraying.

(b) How many ml of chemical are needed to water a 150 m^2 lawn?

(c) How many ml of chemical are needed to spray a 150 m^2 lawn?

(d) About how many times cheaper is it to spray the lawn than to water it?

(e) Copy and complete this information for the bottle label:

Contents 540 ml.

Sufficient to cover ... m^2 (watering-can) or ... m^2 (sprayer).

13 Roy's car has a 1.6 litre, or 1600 cc (cubic centimetres), engine.

Each piston sucks 400 cc of petrol and air mixture into each cylinder, and $\frac{1}{16\,000}$ of the mixture is petrol.

(a) How many ml of petrol are sucked into each cylinder (as a common fraction)?

(b) The car travels 1 km every 2000 turns of the engine, and the mixture is sucked into a cylinder every other turn. How many ml of petrol are used by a cylinder in 1 km?

(c) How many litres of petrol will all four cylinders use in 100 km?

(d) Taking 1 litre = 0.22 gallons and 8 km = 5 miles, find to the nearest whole number the petrol consumption of the car in miles per gallon.

Using your calculator

Keeping slim

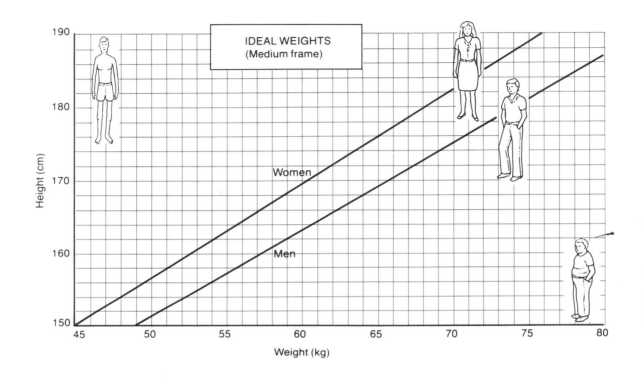

The graph shows ideal weights. You may add up to 10% (one tenth) for a 'large frame' and subtract 10% for a 'small frame'.

HOW TO PUT ON WEIGHT

Eat 100 calories more per day than you need and you put on 90 g per week.

HOW TO LOSE WEIGHT

Eat	LOSS PER YEAR
One less slice of bread a day.	$2\frac{3}{4}$ kg
One less pint of beer a week	1 kg
Eight less crisps a week.	$\frac{1}{2}$ kg
Three less slices of bacon a week	1 kg
Two less doughnuts a week	$1\frac{3}{4}$ kg
Three less teaspoonfuls of sugar a day.	2 kg
One less piece of cake a week	$2\frac{1}{4}$ kg

Count Calories
Chicken (half); grilled 257   fried 464
Cereal (bowl); cornflakes 100   muesli 275
Pudding; baked apple 160   apple pie 410
Cutting 500 calories a day could lose you $\frac{1}{2}$ kg a week.

Exercise
Jog/Run on the spot/Cycle . . . burn up 8 calories per minute.
Walk (fast)/Swim (at 30 m/min) . . . burn up 6 calories per minute.

Ideal aim
Lose $\frac{3}{4}$ kg per week until you reach your ideal weight.

Hints
Drink a glass of water before meals; eat slowly; eat food that needs a lot of chewing. Avoid 'crash-dieting'.

Use the given information and your calculator to answer the following questions.

1   What is an ideal weight for the following medium-frame people:
    (a) man, 150 cm   (b) lady, 150 cm   (c) man, 165 cm   (d) lady, 170 cm
    (e) man, 182 cm?

2   A man is 175 cm tall. He considers he has a large frame. What is his ideal weight?

3   How many kg would you put on in a year if you ate 500 more calories per day than your body needed?

4   If you cut down by one slice of bread a day, sixteen less crisps a week, one less doughnut a week and one less piece of cake a week, how much could you lose in a year?

5   How many calories would you save by eating a half-chicken grilled instead of fried?

6   By eating a bowl of cornflakes each day instead of a bowl of muesli, how many grams could you expect to lose each week? How many kg in a year?

7   If you jog for 20 minutes a day, how many kg could you expect to lose in a year?

8   If your aim is to lose $\frac{3}{4}$ kg a week, how many kg would you expect to lose in a year? Suggest various ways to lose this amount.

A   Finding the circumference, $\pi \simeq 3.14$

> The circumference of a circle is π(pi) multiplied by the diameter (d).
> We write this as $c = \pi d$.
>
> π cannot be found exactly. It is about 3.14

1 Using $\pi = 3.14$ find the circumference of a circle with:
(a) diameter 5 cm   (b) radius 8 cm.

*2 Find the circumference of each circle in figure 31:1. Take $\pi = 3.1$

(a) 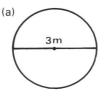   (b)   (c)   (d)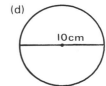

3m   9cm   9m   10cm

Fig. 31:1

3 Taking $\pi = 3.14$ find the circumference of a circular object (e.g. a coin or a tin lid) as accurately as possible.

Check your answer by a practical means.

4 Example   To calculate the perimeter of the shape in Figure 31:2.

The perimeter is the distance all round a shape.

In Figure 31:2 the perimeter is made up of half the circumference of a circle of diameter 2 m and three straight lines:

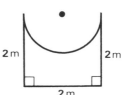

2 m   2 m

2 m

Fig. 31:2

Circumference of circle = 3.14 × 2 = 6.28 m
Half circumference   = 3.14 m
Perimeter of figure   = 3.14 + 2 + 2 + 2 = 9.14 m

1 592 653 589 793 238 462 643 383 279 502 88

Calculate the perimeter of each shape in Figure 31:3 correct to 2 decimal places. Take $\pi = 3.14$

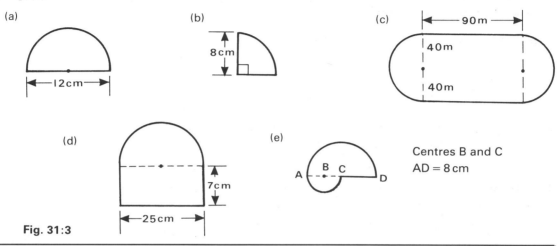

(a)

(b)

(c)

(d)

(e)   Centres B and C
      $AD = 8$ cm

Fig. 31:3

5 The minute hand of a clock is 23 cm long and the hour hand is 17 cm long, both measured from their centre of rotation to their tips.

Using $\pi = 3.14$ find:

(a) how far the tip of the minute hand travels in one hour

(b) how far it travels in one day, in metres correct to 2 d.p.

(c) how far the tip of the hour hand travels in 12 hours

(d) how far it travels in one hour, in cm correct to the nearest mm.

6 Buffon's Needle

Cut a piece of straw 2.5 cm long and mark a piece of paper with parallel lines at 5 cm intervals.

Throw the straw 100 times so that it lands on the paper in a random manner.

Count the number of times that the straw crosses a line.

Divide the number of throws (100) by the number of times that the straw crosses a line.

Repeat the experiment several times.

Comment on your results.

7 The series given in line 6 of this computer program eventually sums to an approximation for π. In order to reach the approximation fairly quickly, line 100 prints the mean average of every pair of terms.

```
  5  REM "Pi 1"
  6  PRINT "Pi by 4*(1 − 1/3 + 1/5 − 1/7 + 1/9 − 1/11 . . .)"
 10  LET X = 1
 20  LET Y = 3
 30  FOR A = 1 TO 100
 40  FOR B = 1 TO 20
 50  LET X = X − 1/Y
 60  LET Z = X
 70  LET Y = Y + 2
 80  LET X = X + 1/Y
 90  LET Y = Y + 2
100  PRINT (Z + X)*2
110  NEXT B
120  CLS    (Clear screen. May not be needed.)
130  NEXT A
```

Note
BBC computer needs
7 PRINT CHR$(14)
to set paging mode.

B Finding the circumference, $\pi \simeq \frac{22}{7}$

The fraction $3\frac{1}{7}$ or $\frac{22}{7}$ is often used as a close approximation for π.

The fraction $\frac{355}{113}$ is a much closer approximation, but makes the arithmetic harder. Note the pattern 113355 which makes it easy to remember.

1 Taking $\pi = \frac{22}{7}$ calculate the circumference of a circle with:
(a) diameter 7 cm   (b) diameter 21 cm   (c) radius 4 cm.

6 406 286 208 998 628 034 825 342 117 067 98

*2 Find the circumference of each wheel shown in Figure 31:4. Take $\pi = \frac{22}{7}$.

(a)
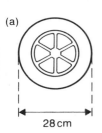

(b)
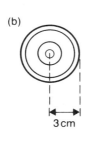

(c)
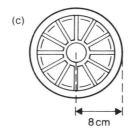

(d)
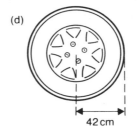

(e)
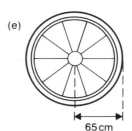

| 28 cm | 3 cm | 8 cm | 42 cm | 65 cm |

Fig. 31:4

*3 Find the circumference of each wheel in Figure 31:4, taking $\pi = 3.1$

*4 How far will the wheels in Figure 31:4 travel in ten turns? (Use your answers to question 3.)

*5 Write your answers to question 4(a) to (d) in metres, and your answer to question 4(e) in kilometres, in each case correct to 1 decimal place.

6 Taking $\pi = 3\frac{1}{7}$ find how many kilometres a 63 cm diameter wheel will travel in:
(a) a thousand revolutions   (b) a million revolutions.

7 The diameter of the Earth is about 12 740 km.

Taking $\pi = 3\frac{1}{7}$ find:

(a) the length of the equator

(b) the speed of a tree on the equator, correct to the nearest 10 km/h.

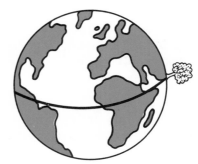

Fig. 31:5

8 A circular bicycle track has an inner radius of 60 m and is 10 m wide. Taking $\pi = 3.14$ find how much farther a cyclist travels on the outside edge than on the inside edge in one lap.

2 148 086 513 282 306 647 093 844 ....!!!

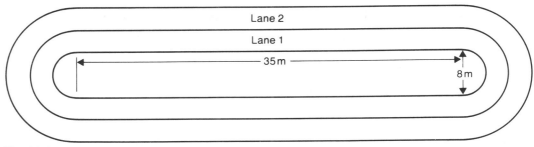

Fig. 31:6

9 Figure 31:6 illustrates a running track. Each lane is 1 metre wide.

The inside edge of the track has 35 m straights and 8 m diameter semi-circular ends.

(a) Find the perimeter of the inside edge of lane 1.

(b) Find the perimeter of the inside edge of lane 2.

(c) How is this difference allowed for on a running track?

---

10 A trundle wheel turns 1000 times in 1 km.

What is its radius?

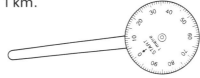

11 A piece of string just fits round a circle of 10 cm radius. How much longer must the string be if it is to lie 5 cm away from the circumference of the circle? Take $\pi = 3.14$

12 A piece of string just fits round the equator. How much longer must the string be to be raised 5 cm above the equator for its entire circumference? Take π to be 3.14 and the radius of the Earth to be 12 740 km.

13 Compare $\frac{22}{7}$ and $\frac{355}{113}$ with the value of π given in the heading to exercise 31A.

14 Space eight points equally round a circle. How many different rectangles can be made by joining four points? Repeat for other numbers of points. Is there a rule?

32 Statistics: mode and median

A The mode

The mode is the item that occurs most frequently in a set of results.

There can be more than one mode.

Examples   The mode for 1, 2, 2, 2, 3, 3, 4 is 2.

The modes for a, a, a, b, c, c, d, g, g, g, h, h are a and g.

When you have a large number of results in a jumbled order, the easiest way to count how many there are of each result is to use a **tally**.

Example   To find the mode of 1, 9, 6, 4, 4, 7, 5, 4, 1, 6, 9, 4, 4, 6, 9, 4, 1.

Item	Tally	Frequency
1	///	3
9	///	3
6	///	3
4	### /	6
7	/	1
5	/	1
Check total		17

→ **The mode is 4.**

1   Find the modes for the following.

(a) 3, 5, 4, 2, 1, 3, 2, 1, 4, 2, 3, 5, 1, 2, 1, 4, 3, 1, 5, 4, 2, 1.

(b) 1, 4, 2, 3, 5, 5, 4, 1, 2, 5, 4, 1, 5, 3, 5, 4, 2, 5, 1, 5, 4, 4, 3.

(c) a, b, c, a, c, d, e, a, c, b, e, d, a, c, d, a, b, e, a, c, a.

*2   Find the modal temperatures for April if the daily readings in °C were:
6, 7, 13, 12, 12, 15, 12, 10, 10, 12, 14, 16, 14, 13, 16, 16, 16, 13, 14, 12, 12, 11, 15, 14, 11, 14, 13, 14, 11, 8.

3   Calculate, as mixed numbers, the means for the data in question 1(a) and (b) and question 2.

4 Copy and complete this tally-chart for the following data about the time taken to complete a test.

Times (min): 24, 28, 26, 25, 28, 30, 29, 27, 24, 30, 16, 24, 28, 29, 27, 28, 24, 27, 28, 29, 29, 29, 39, 29, 27, 29, 29, 27, 29, 30.

Time (T)	Tally	Frequency (F)	T × F
24			
28			

(a) State the mode.

(b) Find the mean by:
   (i) completing the $T \times F$ column
   (ii) summing this column to find the total time
   (iii) dividing by the sum of F.

B The median

When a set of scores is arranged in order the median is the middle score if there is an odd number of scores, or is taken as the mean of the two middle ones if there is an even number of scores.

Examples 2, 2, 3, 9, 17   The median is 3.

3, 4, 7, 7, 8, 9   The median is the mean of 7 and 7 = 7.

2, 4, 7, 8, 9, 9   The median is the mean of 7 and 8 = $\frac{15}{2} = 7\frac{1}{2}$.

Note When the results are not in order it is best to copy them as given, then rewrite them in order, crossing out each copied one as you come to it.

1 Rewrite in order then find the median of:

(a) 3, 2, 5, 4, 1, 4, 3, 4, 1   (b) 1, 3, 5, 2, 4, 5, 7, 8, 1, 4, 4

(c) 2, 2, 4, 4, 5, 7   (d) 7, 8, 7, 3, 4, 7   (e) 6, 8, 0, 3, 5, 7, 3, 0

(f) 2, 7, 2, 8, 5, 9   (g) 6, 4, 2, 8, 5, 9   (h) 9, 5, 12, 3, 8, 4.

*2 Rewrite in order then find the median of:

(a) 1, 9, 9, 7, 4, 3, 2   (b) 4, 4, 7, 9, 3, 2, 6   (c) 9, 3, 8, 7, 5, 4

(d) 12, 20, 21, 2, 12, 16, 20, 21   (e) 2, 7, 1, 6, 5, 9, 0, 8   (f) 4, 7, 2, 8, 7, 2.

3 Find the modes for questions 1 and 2, using ordered lists.

4 Find the means for question 1.

5 Nine men receive in wages:
£90, £100, £100, £100, £110, £110, £112, £115, £360.

Find the median wage, the modal wage and the mean wage.

Which average gives a misleading picture of the nine men's wages? Why does this happen?

6 The median for a large sample is best found from a tally-chart. Note that the scores must be in order.

Example

Score	Tally	Total	Cumulative Total
1	⁂ ⁂	10	10
2	⁂ /	6	16
3	///	3	19
4	⁂ ////	9	28
5	⁂ //	7	35
6	//	2	37
7	//	2	39
8	//	2	41

There are 41 scores so the middle one is the 21st.

19 scores up to here.

The 21st must be one of these.

The median is 4.

Find the median of:

(a) 1, 2, 4, 3, 5, 1, 5, 4, 5, 2, 4, 1, 1, 7, 2, 1, 4, 2, 1, 2, 4, 1, 3, 1, 4, 2, 1, 5, 1, 4, 1, 5, 6, 1, 4, 7, 5, 4, 1, 5, 1, 2, 4, 4, 2, 4, 3, 4, 2, 1, 4, 2, 3, 4, 5, 1, 2, 5, 4, 6, 7, 6, 4, 3, 4, 3, 4.

(b) 9, 8, 6, 12, 7, 8, 9, 10, 12, 9, 8, 9, 10, 11, 8, 9, 6, 7, 9, 12, 11, 8, 9, 6, 9, 12, 8, 7, 9, 6, 9, 9, 8, 10.

7 Write about the uses of averages in everyday life.

A   Cuboids

> **The volume of a cuboid is base area multiplied by height.**

Example   The cuboid in Figure 33:1 has:
Length = 6 cm;
Breadth = 3 cm;
Height = 2 cm.

Its base area = 6 cm × 3 cm = 18 cm².

Its volume = 18 cm² × 2 cm = 36 cm³.

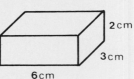

Fig. 33:1

1   Calculate the volume of each cuboid in Figure 33:2.

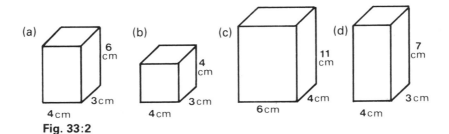

Fig. 33:2

2   Find the volume of each cuboid in Figure 33:3 if each cube is 1 cm³.

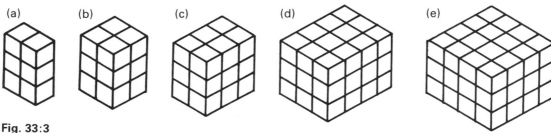

Fig. 33:3

*3 Find (a) to (l) in the following table which gives measurements of cuboids.

Length	4 cm	2 cm	5 cm	7 cm	6 cm	2 cm	3 cm	(h)	6 cm	(j)	7 cm	5 cm
Breadth	2 cm	4 cm	6 cm	5 cm	3 cm	7 cm	2 cm	4 cm	2 cm	1 cm	(k)	(l)
Height	4 cm	1 cm	2 cm	3 cm	5 cm	6 cm	(g)	5 cm	(i)	5 cm	2 cm	5 cm
Volume	(a)	(b)	(c)	(d)	(e)	(f)	36 cm³	120 cm³	144 cm³	20 cm³	70 cm³	125 cm³

4   A container which is a cube of side 10 cm has a volume of 1000 cm³ or 1 litre. What is the capacity in litres of a cuboid 20 cm by 20 cm by 30 cm?

5   What is the capacity in litres of a cuboid 70 cm by 50 cm by 30 cm?

6   How many 2 cm-sided cubes can be put in a box 10 cm long, 8 cm wide and 12 cm high?

7   How many of the packets of SUDS shown in Figure 33:4 can be packed in a box 1.20 m long, 90 cm wide and 80 cm high?

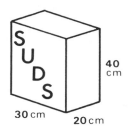

Fig. 33:4   30 cm   40 cm   20 cm

8   A tank can hold 180 litres when full. It is 90 cm long and 50 cm wide. How high is it?

9   How high is an empty room if it is 4 m long and 3 m wide and contains 30 m³ of air?

10   Ali's new house-extension requires a concrete base 3 m long, 5 m wide and 15 cm deep. How many cubic metres of ready-mix concrete should he order?

11   A water-tank measuring 1.2 m × 1 m × 80 cm is half full. How many times could an 8 litre watering-can be filled from it?

12   Water flows at 2 m/s through a pipe of rectangular cross-section 20 cm by 12 cm. How many m³ are delivered per minute?

13   By making suitable measurements find the speed of the water flow through a pipe feeding a tap when the tap is fully open.

B   Volumes of prisms

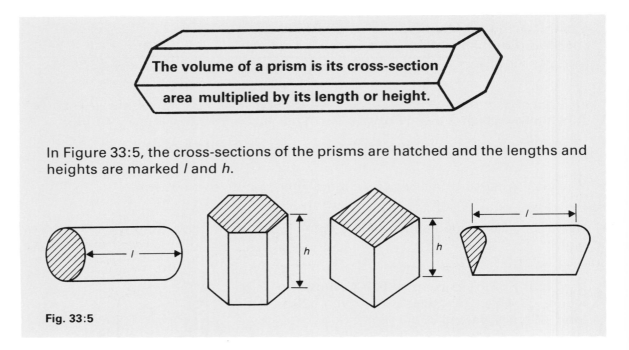

The volume of a prism is its cross-section area multiplied by its length or height.

In Figure 33:5, the cross-sections of the prisms are hatched and the lengths and heights are marked *l* and *h*.

Fig. 33:5

1   Figure 33:6 shows the cross-sections of four prisms, each of height 7 cm. Calculate the volume of each prism.

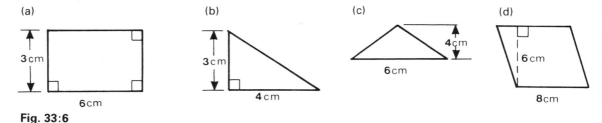

(a)   3 cm   6 cm

(b)   3 cm   4 cm

(c)   4 cm   6 cm

(d)   6 cm   8 cm

Fig. 33:6

*2   Figure 33:7 shows the view looking directly at the end of four prisms, each 6 cm long. Calculate the volume of each prism.

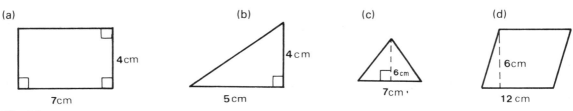

(a)   4 cm   7 cm

(b)   4 cm   5 cm

(c)   6 cm   7 cm

(d)   6 cm   12 cm

Fig. 33:7

3 Draw views like those in Figure 33:5 for the prisms in question 1.

4 Figure 33:8 shows the cross-section of a girder. The measurements are in centimetres. Calculate the volume of the girder in cm³ if it is 4 metres long.

Fig. 33:8

5 An ingot of gold is a cuboid 20 cm by 12 cm by 8 cm. Calculate its mass in kg. (1 cm³ of gold has a mass of about 17.5 g.)

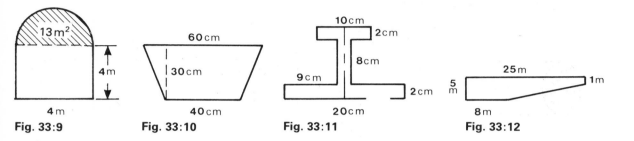

Fig. 33:9 Fig. 33:10 Fig. 33:11 Fig. 33:12

6 Figure 33:9 shows the cross-section of a tunnel 120 m long. What volume of rock was removed?

7 Figure 33:10 shows the cross-section of a trough 6 m long. What is its capacity in litres?

8 Figure 33:11 shows the cross-section of a steel girder. 1 cm³ of steel has a mass of 7.5 g. What is the mass of a seven-metre length of the girder?

9 Figure 33:12 shows the cross-section of a swimming pool which is 8 metres wide. How much water is in the pool when it is full, both in m³ and in litres?

10 Find the value of the gold ingot in question 5.

11 Collect prism-shaped boxes. Calculate their volumes and check your answers practically.

12 Make the prisms shown in question 2, using either card, or pipe-cleaners and straws.

A Similar and congruent figures

Figures or objects are **similar** if one is an exact enlargement of the other. Figures or objects are **congruent** if one is exactly the same shape and size as the other.

Pairs of corresponding lengths of similar figures are in the same ratio.
Pairs of corresponding sides and angles in congruent figures are equal.

For Discussion

Which of the pairs of figures in Figure 34:1 are similar?
Which pairs are congruent?

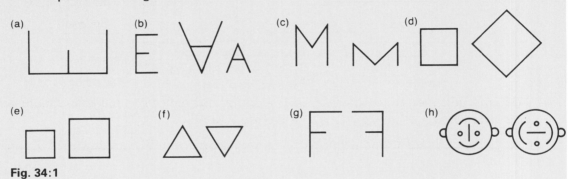

Fig. 34:1

1 Draw three shapes like those in Figure 34:2, but change the lengths in the given ratios. Write the new lengths on your figures.

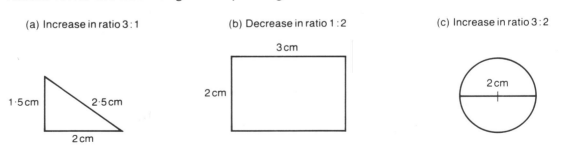

(a) Increase in ratio 3 : 1   (b) Decrease in ratio 1 : 2   (c) Increase in ratio 3 : 2

Fig. 34:2

2 Figure 34:3 shows how similar shapes can be drawn using 'rays' from a point. The point can be inside the figure, on an edge, on a corner, or outside the shape.

(a) Copy the diagrams in Figure 34:3. The sides need not be in any special ratio.

(b) Repeat the four diagrams for a shape of your own.

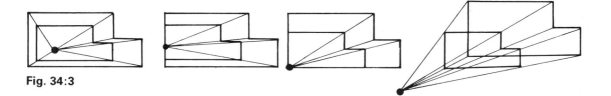

Fig. 34:3

3 Another way of drawing similar shapes is by using a grid of squares, as shown in Figure 34:4.

Use 1 cm-squared paper to copy Figure 34:4 with all lengths increased in the ratio 2:1.

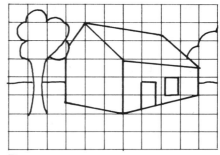

Fig. 34:4

4 Use the grid method to copy (giving a congruent picture) a magazine picture. Use the same method to enlarge or reduce a picture.

B Lengths' ratio of similar figures

For Discussion

Which shapes in Figures 34:5 and 34:6 are similar?

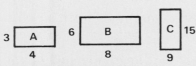

Fig. 34:5 (Not to scale)

Fig. 34:6 (Not to scale)

1 Copy and complete:
    (a) 1:4 = 5:   (b)   :2 = 6:4   (c) 6:12 = 12:

2 State the ratio of the lengths of each pair of similar shapes in Figure 34:7, reduced to its lowest terms (i.e. as simply as possible).

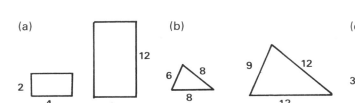

Fig. 34:7

3 Which of the pairs of shapes in Figure 34:8 are similar?

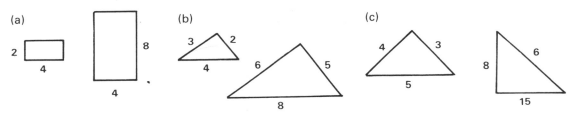

Fig. 34:8

*4 Where the pairs of shapes in Figure 34:9 are similar, state the ratio of their sides as simply as possible.

    Where they are not similar, say so.

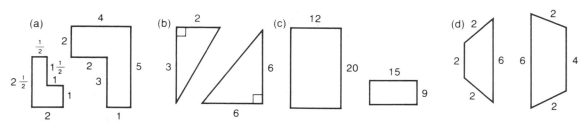

Fig. 34:9

5 All the pairs of figures in Figure 34:10 are similar. By finding the ratios of pairs of corresponding (in the same position) sides, calculate the values of a to q.

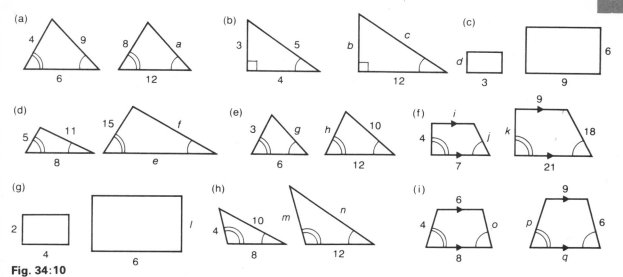

Fig. 34:10

6 Example

Fig. 34:11

The two triangles in Figure 34:11 are similar.

Their sides are in the ratio 3:1.

But their areas are in the ratio 9:1.

Draw the figures in Figure 34:12 to the exact sizes given.

Then draw similar figures with sides enlarged in the given ratios. By drawing, as in the example, find the ratios of their areas.

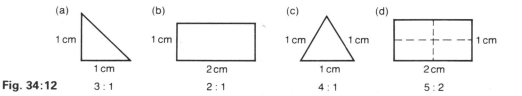

Fig. 34:12

7 From your answers to question 6, find the rule to calculate the areas' ratio given the sides' ratio.

Calculate the areas' ratio if the sides' ratio is:
(a) 10:1   (b) 100:1   (c) 3:2   (d) 4:7   (e) 4.6:7.9   (f) $x:y$.

A Decimal fractions

Do you need to practise? Try to answer questions 1 to 8 without **help** and without a calculator.

1 Add 4.28, 36, 41.3 and 0.586   **2** Take 3.91 from 15.60

3 Take 9.99 from 30   **4** Add one tenth to 2.9

5 Take one hundredth from 16   **6** 4.8×3.7

7 2.01×10 **8** (a) $3.6 \div 5$ (b) $4.14 \div 0.6$

For practice on questions 1 to 7 see exercise 5A, questions 1 to 16.

For practice on question 8 see exercise 5C, questions 1 to 3.

9 Copy and complete the table.

Number	6	7.4	83.1	0.4	0.08
$\times 10$ $\times 100$ $\div 10$ $\div 100$					

10 **Example**   To work out $47.6 \times 2\,000\,000$

First ignore the noughts and the point, and work out 476×2, giving 952

Then replace the noughts, giving $952\,000\,000$

Finally insert the point by the usual rule, giving $95\,200\,000.0$

The final nought is not really needed, so write the answer as $95\,200\,000$

Give answers to the following without a decimal point.
(a) 72.3×200 (b) 4.75×3000 (c) 26.8×500 (d) $6.3 \times 20 \times 100$
(e) $4.9 \times 10 \times 200\,000$

11 Example $0.035 = \dfrac{35}{1000} \rightarrow \dfrac{7}{200}.$

What simple rule tells you to write 1000 at the bottom?

Write as simplified fractions or mixed numbers:
(a) 0.025   (b) 0.45   (c) 0.04   (d) 1.05   (e) 4.35   (f) 7.0125

12 Give answers to the following correct to 2 decimal places. (In the divisions, stop when you reach the third figure after the point, the 'key' figure.)
(a) 4.7×0.25 (b) 0.9×0.11 (c) $1 \div 7$ (d) $1 \div 6$ (e) $\frac{1}{16}$

---

13 Example $\dfrac{1765 \times 149}{19.5}$ is very approximately $\dfrac{2000 \times 100}{20}$
$\rightarrow 100 \times 100 = 10\,000.$

Work in a similar way to find approximate answers to:

(a) $\dfrac{5123 \times 86}{8.8}$ (b) $\dfrac{623 \times 35}{29.4}$ (c) $\dfrac{3.75 \times 210}{410}$

(d) $\dfrac{17.7 \times 3.8}{0.14}$ (e) $\dfrac{61.5 \times 0.29}{0.026}$ (f) $\dfrac{1555 \times 0.38}{6.3}$

14 Work out question 13 accurately using a calculator. Then make up some more questions and work out the answers approximately. Finally work out these answers accurately.

15 Using the figures 0 to 9 once only, write correct addition sums. You must use all ten figures. You could write the ones you find on a wall poster. We have found 60. Can you find more? Write and tell us if you do.

Example $753 + 849 = 1602$

B Common fractions

Do you need to practise?

Try to answer questions 1 to 6 without help. Give each answer as a fraction or mixed number, as simply as possible.

1 $1\frac{3}{8} + 2\frac{1}{8}$ **2** $\frac{5}{6} - \frac{7}{9}$ **3** $12\frac{3}{5} - 9\frac{3}{4}$

4 $\frac{3}{7} \times 2$ **5** $3 \times \frac{2}{9}$ **6** $\frac{11}{16} \times 12$

For practice on	See exercise	Questions
Question 1	20B	1 to 5
Question 2	20C	1 to 8
Question 3	20D	1 to 5
Questions 4 to 6	See question 7 below.	

7 Examples   (i) $\dfrac{3}{5} \times \dfrac{2}{7} = \dfrac{6}{35}$ (ii) $\dfrac{^1 3}{_1 5} \times \dfrac{10^2}{21_7} = \dfrac{2}{7}$

(iii) $1\dfrac{1}{9} \times 3\dfrac{1}{2} \;\rightarrow\; \dfrac{^5 10}{9} \times \dfrac{7}{2_1} = \dfrac{35}{9} = 3\dfrac{8}{9}$

(a) $\dfrac{4}{7} \times \dfrac{2}{3}$ (b) $\dfrac{3}{8} \times \dfrac{2}{7}$ (c) $16 \times \dfrac{3}{5}$ (d) $16 \times \dfrac{3}{8}$ (e) $\dfrac{4}{6} \times \dfrac{3}{5}$ (f) $\dfrac{4}{12} \times \dfrac{12}{16}$

8   (a) $3\dfrac{3}{5} \times 4\dfrac{1}{6}$ (b) $3\dfrac{3}{5} + 4\dfrac{1}{6}$ (c) $4\dfrac{1}{6} - 3\dfrac{3}{5}$ (d) $1\dfrac{1}{8} + \dfrac{11}{12}$

9   (a) $1\dfrac{1}{8} \times \dfrac{7}{12}$ (b) $1\dfrac{1}{8} - \dfrac{7}{12}$ (c) $3\dfrac{3}{5} \times 1\dfrac{5}{6}$ (d) $3\dfrac{2}{5} - 1\dfrac{5}{6}$

Fig. 35:1

10 Example   In Figure 35:1,

if the ratio of the areas A:B = 7:5

then A is $\dfrac{7}{12}$ of the whole rectangle and A is $\dfrac{7}{5}$ of B

and B is $\dfrac{5}{12}$ of the whole rectangle and B is $\dfrac{5}{7}$ of A

If the ratio of the areas A:B = 7:5, calculate for Figure 35:1
(a) the area of A   (b) the area of B.

11 If, for Figure 35:1, the areas A:B = 5:3, then:

(a) what fraction of the whole rectangle is A

(b) what fraction of the whole rectangle is B

(c) what fraction of B is A   (d) what fraction of A is B

(e) what is the area of A   (f) what is the area of B?

12 Investigate the use of a calculator for questions 7 to 9.

Project

Modulos

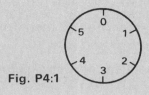
1 Using the modulo clock in Figure P4:2, change to modulo 5:
(a) 7   (b) 9   (c) 3   (d) 15   (e) 57
(f) 68.

Fig. P4:2

2 If we start at any number and add 1 (mod 5) we can obtain Figure P4:3.
Draw a similar diagram for 'add 2 (mod 5)'.
(Hint: 0 to 2, 2 to 4, 4 to 1, etc.)
Draw the diagram for 'add 3' and 'add 4' in modulo 5.

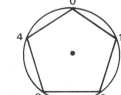

Fig. P4:3

3 Investigate other modulo patterns.

4 If $x \in$ {numbers in mod 12} find four solutions to $4x = 4$ and three solutions to $9x = 6$.

5 Divide the circumference of a circle into twelve parts.

Mark it for mod 12 then draw a number chain for $\times 2$ (mod 12). (Hint: Join 0 to 2, 2 to 4, 4 to 6, 6 to 8, 8 to 10, 10 to 0.)

Repeat with new circles for $\times 3$, $\times 4$ and $\times 5$ in mod 12.

6 Copy and complete this table in mod 36 for 'multiplied by 2'.

x	0	1	2	3	4	5	6	7	8... up to 35
$2x$	0	2	4	6	8	10	12	14	16...

Draw a large circle. Use a protractor to divide it into 36 equal divisions. Join the corresponding values in the table, i.e. 0 to 0, 1 to 2, 2 to 4, etc.

The curve you should have drawn is a **cardioid**.

7 Use a similar method to that in question 6 for 'multiplied by 3' and 'multiplied by 4' in modulo 72. You should obtain curves called a **nephroid** and a **trefoil**.

8 A mod 13 slide rule can be made from a 3 cm-radius card disc, an 8 cm square of card and a 'point-up' drawing pin. In Figure P4:4 the slide rule shows the result of adding 6, for example $6 + 9 = 2$ and $6 + 7 = 0$.
Make a slide rule and learn to use it for addition and subtraction in modulo 13.

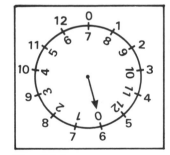

Fig. P4:4

9 Figure P4:5 shows a slide rule to multiply in mod 7. It is set up to multiply by 3, for example $3 \times 5 = 1$ and $3 \times 6 = 4$.

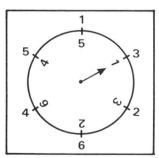

Fig. P4:5

10 A slide rule for mod 13 multiplication can be made using the numbers 1, 2, 4, 8, 3, 6, 12, 11, 9, 5, 10 and 7 in that order.

Papers

Paper 1

1 Calculate the perimeter and the area of a rectangle 2.7 cm long and 2.3 cm wide.

2 Draw up the two route matrices for the networks in Figure P1.

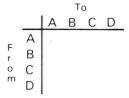

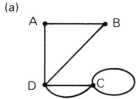 (a)

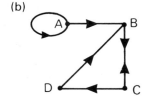 (b)

Fig. P1

*3 In Figure P2 all the short lines are the same length.

Calculate:

(a) the length of one short side in cm

(b) the perimeter of the shape in metres

(c) the area of the shape in m².

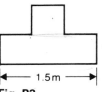

Fig. P2

*4 A scale of 1:100 means that 1 cm on the drawing is really 100 cm on the actual object.

(a) How many cm on the actual object is represented by a drawn line of length:
(i) 2 cm   (ii) 1.5 cm   (iii) 2.63 cm?

(b) Rewrite your answers to part (a) in metres.

*5 **Example** $\frac{3}{3} = 1$, so $\frac{6}{3} = 2$. Similarly $\frac{5}{3} = 1\frac{2}{3}$.

Write either as an integer or as a mixed number:
(a) $\frac{5}{5}$ (b) $\frac{10}{5}$ (c) $\frac{6}{5}$ (d) $\frac{11}{5}$ (e) $\frac{8}{7}$ (f) $\frac{9}{5}$ (g) $\frac{17}{4}$ (h) $\frac{25}{6}$.

6 Simplify the following fractions by 'cancelling'.
(a) $\frac{2}{8}$ (b) $\frac{21}{56}$ (c) $\frac{24}{64}$ (d) $\frac{1392}{600}$

7 Write a brief explanation of the meaning of:
(a) the origin of a graph   (b) the *x*-axis   (c) a regular pentagon
(d) an equivalent fraction   (e) the Fibonacci sequence   (f) a prime number.

8 First rewrite the amounts in kg, then find the sum of:
1000 g, 500 g, 650 g, 31 250 g, 25 g, 10 g.

9 Show how to cut a triangle into three pieces that can be re-assembled, without turning them over, to give a mirror image of the triangle. (It may help you to draw the triangle with its sides touching a circle.)

10 Draw 25 small squares arranged in one large square. Mark dots at the centres of fifteen of the small squares so that there are no more than three dots in a straight line.

Paper 2

1 Name:

(a) the horizontal axis on a graph   (b) the point (0, 0) where the axes of a graph cross

(c) a regular triangle   (d) a regular quadrilateral

(e) a regular polygon with five sides.

*2 **Example** $\frac{18}{24} = \frac{3}{4}$ (Dividing the 18 and the 24 by 6.)

Simplify:
(a) $\frac{8}{12}$ (b) $\frac{16}{20}$ (c) $\frac{30}{40}$ (d) $\frac{48}{60}$ (e) $\frac{35}{42}$ (f) $\frac{56}{80}$.

*3 Copy the following Fibonacci Sequence and write the next four numbers: 1, 1, 2, 3, 5, . . .

*4 Which of the following are prime numbers? 2, 5, 9, 11, 15, 21.

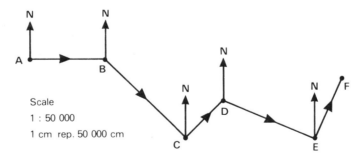

Scale
1 : 50 000
1 cm rep. 50 000 cm

Fig. P3

5 State for the journey shown in Figure P3:

(a) the distances in km between each of the points A to F

(b) the bearing taken at each point as both a cardinal and a three-figure bearing, e.g. (D: ESE; $112\frac{1}{2}°$).

6 Divide each integer from 1 to 20 by 9. Give answers as recurring decimals, e.g. 0.1̇

7 Of sixty people on a train, ten are under-fives, twenty-five are between five and eighteen and the rest are over eighteen. Draw a pie-chart to illustrate this data, marking the three angles used on the chart.

8 How many times do the hands of a clock pass one another between 1415 Monday and 1415 Tuesday?

Paper 3

1 **Example** By measuring with a protractor, angle θ in Figure P4 is 30°.

So A is on a bearing of 330° from B.

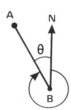

Fig. P4

Find each bearing of A from B in Figure P5.

(a)
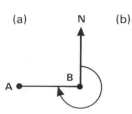

(b)
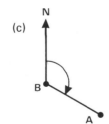

(c)
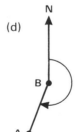

(d) (e)
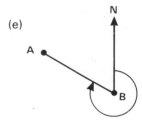

Fig. P5

*2 If 1 cm is to represent 10 km, draw a line to represent 8 km. Write under your line how many cm long you have drawn it.

*3 **Examples** 0.333333 . . . is written 0.3̇

0.15151515 . . . is written 0.1̇5̇

0.127127127 . . . is written 0.1̇27̇

These are called **recurring decimals**.

Use the dot method for:
(a) 0.666666 . . .   (b) 0.212121 . . .   (c) 0.123123123 . . .

*4 Draw a pie-chart to show that, in a class of 36 children, 15 are boys and 21 are girls.

5 If $a = 2$, $b = 1$ and $c = 9$ state the value of:
(a) b^2 (b) c^2 (c) $a^2 + b$ (d) $2b^2 + c$ (e) a^2c.

6 Rewrite the following in order of size from smallest to largest:
0, 1, -8.5, $\frac{1}{2}$, -9, -10, -8.

7 Find:
(a) -3 and -2 (b) $-3 - 2$ (c) $4 - 8$ (d) $8 - 4$ (e) $-7 + 5$.

8 By drawing and measuring find to the nearest mm the length of the chord in a diagram like Figure P6 if the radius of the arc is 4 cm and angle AOB is 90°, where O is the centre.

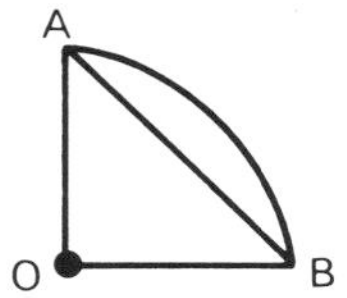

Fig. P6

9 A rectangle has an area of 36 cm². It has integral sides of length s cm and t cm.

(a) Draw up a table to show all possible values of s and t and p (the perimeter of the rectangle).

(b) Draw up a graph of p against s with s horizontal and p vertical.

10 How can you make $\boxed{1 \div 8 = \frac{8}{1}}$ true without changing in any way what is written in the rectangle?

Paper 4

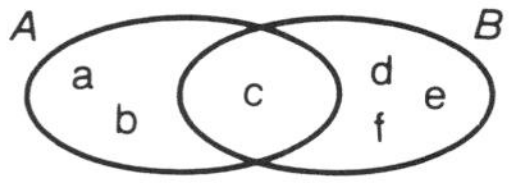

1 (a) Write 'D is a subset of E' using the subset sign.

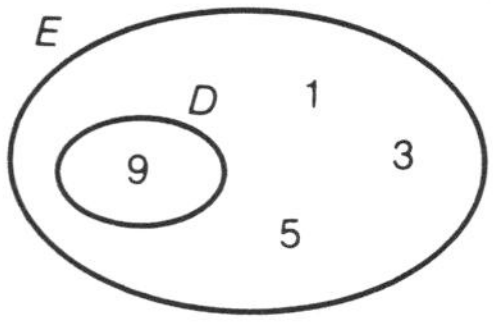

(b) In Figure P7, set $A = \{a, b, c\}$.

List in a similar way for the sets in Figures P7 and P8:
(i) B (ii) D (iii) E.

(c) In Figure P7 there are 3 elements in set A, i.e. $n(A) = 3$.

Using the n( ) notation write for Figures P7 and P8:
(i) $n(B)$ (ii) $n(D)$ (iii) $n(E)$.

(d) What letter is written in the intersection of sets A and B (or A ∩ B)?

(e) The union of A and B is written A ∪ B. List the elements of A ∪ B.

Fig. P7

Fig. P8

2 Which of the following are *not* prime numbers?
2; 3; 5; 7; 9; 11; 13; 15; 17; 19; 21; 23.

3 (a) Write out the multiples of 17 from 17 to 170.
Start your answer: 17, 34, 51, . . .

(b) Find 8636 ÷ 17.

*4 Sketch clearly:
(a) an acute angle, θ   (b) an obtuse angle, φ   (c) a reflex angle, ψ
(Note: θ, φ and ψ are Greek letters, often used in geometry.)

5 $P = \{20°, 82°, 100°, 150°, 250°, 335°\}$
$A = \{$acute angles$\}$; $O = \{$obtuse angles$\}$; $R = \{$reflex angles$\}$.

For the angles listed in set P:
(a) List set A.   (b) List set O.   (c) How many angles in set R?

(d) Is 100° a member of set O?

6 | divide speed by 20 | → | add 2 | → | multiply by speed | → | divide by 10 | → | write answer |

This flow diagram shows how many metres it takes an average car to stop at a given speed in km/h.

(a) How many metres to stop at: (i) 60 km/h   (ii) 120 km/h?

(b) What is the fastest integral speed in km/h at which an average car could stop in 100 metres?

(c) Change your answer to (b) to m.p.h., to the nearest integer. Take 8 km = 5 miles.

7 Copy square ABCD in Figure P9, then draw an equilateral triangle DCE inside the square.

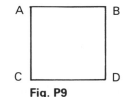

Fig. P9

Paper 5

1 (a) 36 × 29   (b) 36 × 0.29 (use the answer to (a))   (c) 47 ÷ 4 as a decimal fraction.

*2 If $a = 3$ find the value of: (a) a^2 (b) $2a$ (c) $3a$ (d) $3a + 8$ (e) $2a^2$.

*3 (a) 5 − 3   (b) −5 − 3   (c) 3 − 5   (d) −2 − 8   (e) −2 + 8

*4 How many:
(a) integers from 5 to 12 inclusive   (b) integers that divide exactly into 18
(c) cm in 3.4 m   (d) metres in 1.5 km   (e) metres in 1.55 km?

P

*5   Look at Figures P10, P11 and P12.

(a) Which figure shows:
  (i) a subset of a set
  (ii) two disjoint sets
  (iii) two intersecting sets?

(b) Each diagram shows the number of elements in the sets. For example, n(P) = 7.

What is:
(i) n(Q)   (ii) n(X)   (iii) n(Y)
(iv) n(P ∩ Q)   (v) n(P ∪ Q)   (vi) n(X ∪ Y)
(vii) n(A ∪ B)   (viii) n(A ∩ B)?

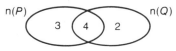

Fig. P10

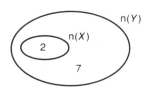

Fig. P11

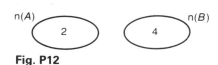

Fig. P12

6   Copy and complete the table.

d	7d	10d	70d	$\frac{d}{8}$	$\frac{d}{10}$	$\frac{d}{80}$
5.6						
0.064						
150						

7   A scale of 1:100 means that 1 cm on the diagram represents a real measurement of 100 cm.

Write in *metres* the distance represented by 1 cm if the scale is:
(a) 1:100   (b) 1:50   (c) 1:200   (d) 1:250.

8   On a scale of 1:50 how many centimetres would represent:
(a) 1 metre   (b) 5 metres   (c) 0.5 metres   (d) 2.5 metres   (e) 5.6 metres
(f) 0.8 metres?

9   A room is 4 metres long, 2.5 metres wide and 1.5 metres high. Draw diagrams of the floor, one longer wall and one shorter wall, neither wall having door or window, to a scale of 1:50.

Paper 6

1   **Example** $8.25 \div 0.5 \rightarrow \frac{8.25}{0.5} \rightarrow \frac{82.5}{5} = 16.5$

(a) $7.25 \div 0.5$ (b) $8.348 \div 0.4$ (c) $12.6 \div 0.3$ (d) $23.43 \div 1.1$ (e) $15.6 \div 0.03$

2   (a) $-3-4$ (b) $3-4$ (c) $-2-7$ (d) $2-7$ (e) $1--2$ (f) $3--4$
(g) $-2--1$ (h) $-7--7$

190

3 (a) $\begin{pmatrix} 1 & 2 & 4 \\ 3 & 0 & 1 \end{pmatrix} + \begin{pmatrix} 2 & 7 & 6 \\ 3 & 1 & 0 \end{pmatrix}$ (b) $\begin{pmatrix} -2 & -3 \\ -1 & 8 \end{pmatrix} + \begin{pmatrix} 6 & 6 \\ 6 & 6 \end{pmatrix}$ (c) $\begin{pmatrix} 2 & 4 \\ 6 & 5 \end{pmatrix} - \begin{pmatrix} 1 & -1 \\ -1 & 1 \end{pmatrix}$

4 Copy the diagrams in Figure P13, then draw the images in the mirror lines, m.

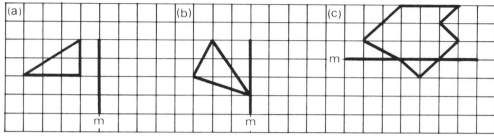

Fig. P13

*5 (a) 17×100 (b) 1.7×10 (c) 1.7×100 (d) 0.17×10 (e) $36 \div 10$
   (f) $360 \div 100$ (g) $3.6 \div 10$ (h) $3.6 \div 100$ (i) $0.3 \div 10$

6 (a) $3.16 + 18 + 0.05$ (b) $117.8 - 70.98$ (c) 4.9×0.87 (d) $1.734 \div 1.7$

7 In Figure P14, I, J, K, L, M and N are the midpoints of the edges of the cube.

Name as precisely as possible (all triangles are special ones) the plane shape made by joining the points:
(a) GJK   (b) NIKM   (c) EHCB
(d) ADMN   (e) NGB   (f) ACGE   (g) FHC
(h) FGL   (i) NML   (j) FNDK.

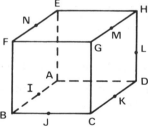

Fig. P14

Paper 7

1 Look at Figures P15, P16 and P17.

(a) Which figure shows:
    (i) two disjoint sets
    (ii) two intersecting sets
    (iii) a set with a subset?

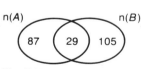

Fig. P15

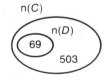

Fig. P16

(b) The number of elements in set A is 116.
    We write $n(A) = 116$.
    What is:
    (i) $n(B)$ (ii) $n(A \cap B)$ (iii) $n(A \cup B)$
    (iv) $n(C)$ (v) $n(D)$ (vi) $n(C \cap D)$
    (vii) $n(C \cup D)$ (viii) $n(E \cap F)$?

Fig. P17

*2 Showing clear methods use a pair of compasses to draw an angle of:
(a) 60°   (b) 30°   (c) 90°.

*3 Using only compasses, a ruler, and a pencil, draw an accurate square of side 4 cm.

Measure a diagonal of your square and write on it its length in cm.

*4 If $x = 3$ state the value of:
(a) x^2 (b) $2x^2$ (c) $x - 3$ (d) $3x - 1$.

*5 Simplify:
(a) $a + a$ (b) $a \times a$ (c) $3a + a$ (d) $a + b + 3b$.

6 (a) Construct $\triangle ABC$ with $AB = 6$ cm and $BC = AC = 4.5$ cm.

(b) Construct the inscribed circle of this isosceles triangle.

7 Simplify:
(a) $8c + c$ (b) $c \times c$ (c) $2a + 3 - a$ (d) $4x + y - 2x + 3y$.

8 If $a = 1$ and $b = 2$ state the value of:
(a) a^2 (b) $2b^2$ (c) a^3 (d) ab.

9 In Britain a car's fuel consumption is usually stated in m.p.g. (miles per gallon). On the continent it is stated in litres/100 km (litres per 100 km).

What would 25 m.p.g. become in litres/100 km? Take 5 miles = 8 km and 1 gallon = 4.5 litres.

Paper 8

1 Use your protractor to draw an accurate angle of: (a) 110°   (b) 45°.

*2 In Figure P18 line AB is divided in the ratio 2:3. How long is AX if AB is 20 cm?

A   X   B

Fig. P18

*3 Calculate the perimeter and the area of a rectangle 8.5 cm long and 3.7 cm wide.

*4 A ferry leaves Dover every 40 minutes. If a ferry leaves Dover at 1130 write as 24-hour-clock times the departure times of the next three ferries.

*5 If $x = 2$ state the value of: (a) x^2 (b) $2x^2$ (c) $x - 3$ (d) $3x + 1$.

6 Construct Figure P19 accurately without using a set-square or a protractor. Show clear compass arcs for the 30° and the 90° angles.

7 cm

Fig. P19

7 Share £84 between two people so that one receives twice as much as the other.

8 A rectangle is 186 mm long and 97 mm wide.

Change these lengths to cm and hence calculate the area of the rectangle in cm².

9 A satellite passes overhead every 11 hours 40 minutes.

If it is overhead on Sunday at 1405, write the days and 24-hour-clock times of the next five times it is overhead.

10 Calculate in m² the area of the rectangle in question 8.

11 A slot-machine takes only 5p and 10p coins.

Using **o** and **O** to show the coins write all possible orders of inserting coins to pay the following amounts.

Example 15p can be paid in the orders: **ooo**; **oO**; **Oo**.

(a) 5p (b) 10p (c) 15p (d) 20p (e) 25p

By considering your answers state how many different orders there will be to pay 50p.

Paper 9

1 (a) Use compasses to construct a triangle with sides of 7 cm, 5 cm and 4 cm.

(b) Bisect the angles of your triangle to find the incentre and draw the incircle.

2 Rewrite in alphabetical order the following expressions.

Example $b - a + 3c \rightarrow -a + b + 3c$

(a) $2x - a + c - 3b$ (b) $4y - 2a + 3k - s$ (c) $-m + 3b - 2a - 4n$

3 Rewrite the following expressions in order of size, smallest first.

Example $1 - 2 - 5 \rightarrow -5 - 2 + 1$

(a) $4 - 7 + 3$ (b) $-2 - 1 - 5$ (c) $-8 + 1 - 1$ (d) $-1 + 5 - 2 - 4 + 2$

4 Figures P20, P21 and P22 show the same triangle rotated so that each side in turn becomes the base.

By measuring and calculation state the base, height and area of the triangle in each of its three positions.

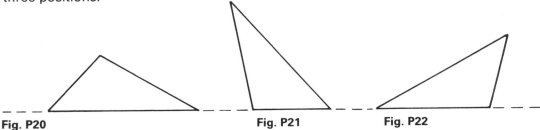

Fig. P20   **Fig. P21**   **Fig. P22**

*5 (a) $-7 - 2$ (b) $7 - 2$ (c) $2 - 7$ (d) -3×-3 (e) $-3 \div -3$
    (f) $12 \div -6$

*6 Example $1 + 6 - 9 = 7 - 9 = -2$

    (a) $2 + 7 - 3$ (b) $4 + 8 - 9$ (c) $1 + 4 - 8$ (d) $3 - 1 - 1$

*7 Find the mean average of 8, 9, 12, 16, 16 and 23.

8 Calculate the value of the expressions in question 3.

   Example $1 - 2 - 5 = -6$

9 If $s = 0.582$ and $t = 0.6$ calculate:
   (a) $s + t$ (b) $t - s$ (c) st (d) $s \div t$ (e) $s - t$.

10 In this question $A \cap B = A$, $C \supset D$, and $E \cap F = \emptyset$.

   (a) Sketch labelled Venn diagrams for each pair of sets.

   (b) Simplify, choosing your answers from C, D, E or $\emptyset$:
        (i) $C \cap D$ (ii) $C \cup D$ (iii) $E \cup \emptyset$ (iv) $A \cap \emptyset$.

Paper 10

1 Example $\dfrac{1}{4} \to \dfrac{1}{4} \times 100\% \to \dfrac{1}{{}_1 4} \times 100^{25}\% = 25\%$

   Example $\dfrac{1}{3} \to \dfrac{1}{3} \times 100\% \to \dfrac{100\%}{3} = 33\tfrac{1}{3}\%$

   Change to a percentage:
   (a) $\tfrac{3}{4}$ (b) $\tfrac{3}{5}$ (c) $\tfrac{2}{3}$ (d) $\tfrac{4}{15}$ (e) $1\tfrac{1}{2}$.

2 Example $12\% = \dfrac{12}{100} \rightarrow \dfrac{3}{25}$ (dividing top and bottom by 4)

Change to a fraction, simplified if possible:
(a) 1%   (b) 15%   (c) 64%   (d) 108%.

3 Find (a), (b), (c), (d), (e) and (f) in this table.

Time	1 h	1 h	2 h	2 h	(c)	2 h	$\frac{1}{2}$ h	$\frac{1}{2}$ h
Distance	40 km	50 km	40 km	50 km	60 km	(d)	6 km	(f)
Speed	40 km/h	(a)	20 km/h	(b)	60 km/h	40 km/h	(e)	15 km/h

*4 Write the name of the polygon with:
(a) 3 sides   (b) 4 sides   (c) 5 sides   (d) 6 sides   (e) 8 sides   (f) 10 sides.

*5 Write the first ten triangular numbers.

6 Copy and complete the tables for the given relations using only 1 and 0. Remember to read the side number before the top one.

(a) 1 shows 'is a factor of'

	6	8	9	15
2	1	1	0	0
3				
6				

(b) 1 shows 'is a prime factor of'

	6	8	9	15
2				
3				
6				

(c) 1 shows 'is smaller than'

	-2	0	$-\frac{1}{4}$	$-1\frac{1}{2}$
2				
0				
-1				

7 List the fractions in question 1 (a) to (e) in order of size from largest to smallest.

8 Work out to the nearest whole number:
(a) $183 \div 7$ (b) $207 \div 0.8$ (c) $4.06 \div 1.3$

9 What fraction of three is the same as one-third of two?

10 Using twelve identical hurdles make six identical sheep pens.

P

Paper 11

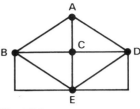

Fig. P23

1 For the network in Figure P23:

(a) State the order of nodes A to E.

(b) How many arcs and how many regions are there in the network?

(c) Is the network traversable (that is, can you draw it with one continuous line without repeating any arcs)?

If not, explain why not. If it is traversable write the nodes you come to in order from start to finish.

(d) Draw up the route matrix for this network.

*2 Copy and complete the mapping for values of x from 1 to 12.

$$x \rightarrow x^2$$
$$1 \rightarrow 1$$
$$2 \rightarrow 4$$
$$3 \rightarrow 9$$
etc.

*3 Simplify:
(a) $x + x$ (b) $x \times x$ (c) $3a - 2a$ (d) $2a + 5a + 7a$ (e) $3a - 2a - a$
(f) $a + a + 1$ (g) $3a + 2a - 1$ (h) $x + 2x + y$.

*4 **Example** $\dfrac{3}{5} \rightarrow 5\overline{)3.0}^{\,0.6}$, so $\dfrac{3}{5} = 0.6$

Change to a decimal fraction:
(a) $\frac{2}{5}$ (b) $\frac{1}{8}$ (c) $\frac{3}{8}$ (d) $\frac{9}{16}$.

*5 Find the sum (+), difference (−), product (×) and quotient (÷) of 14.4 and 0.12. (For the quotient find $14.4 \div 0.12$.)

6 Simplify:
(a) $3a - a + 2$ (b) $4a^2 + a + 3a^2$ (c) $2a^2 - a^2$.

7 If $a = 1$ find the value of (a), (b) and (c) in question 6.

8 If $x = 2.7$ find the value of:
(a) $2x$ (b) x^2 (c) x^3.

9 Change to a decimal fraction:
(a) $1\frac{3}{5}$ (b) $\frac{7}{8}$ (c) $\frac{1}{25}$ (d) $\frac{19}{25}$.

196

10 When an object falls, the distance fallen (*s* metres) in *t* seconds is given by the formula $s = 4.9t^2$.

How far will an object fall in:
(a) 1 sec (b) 2 sec (c) 3 sec (d) 4 sec (e) 5 sec?

Draw a graph with the time (*t*) horizontal and the distance (*s*) vertical, plotting the points given by your answers.

Paper 12

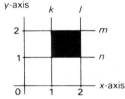

Fig. P24

1 In Figure P24:

(a) Which line has the equation:
(i) $x = 0$ (ii) $y = 0$ (iii) $x = 2$ (iv) $y = 1$?

(b) State the equation of: (i) line *k*   (ii) line *m*.

(c) Which of *A* or *B* is the correct description of the shaded region?

   A $\{(x, y) : 1 < x < 2; 2 < y < 1\}$ B $\{(x, y) : 1 < x < 2; 1 < y < 2\}$

2 The angles of a polygon add up to $(n - 2) \times 180°$ where *n* is the number of sides.

Example   For a pentagon, $n = 5$ so the angle sum is $3 \times 180° = 540°$.

Use the formula to show that the angle sum of a triangle is $180°$ and of a quadrilateral is $360°$, then calculate the angle sum of a hexagon.

3 **Example** $0.56 = \dfrac{56}{100} = \dfrac{14}{25}$ (dividing by 4)

Write as a simplified common fraction: (a) 0.25   (b) 0.80   (c) 0.36   (d) 0.8

4 (a) Draw a line AB, length 4.5 cm, then construct its perpendicular bisector XMY crossing AB at M with XM = MY = 2 cm.

(b) Join A, X, B and Y to make a quadrilateral then calculate its area by using the formula: Area of a triangle is half of the base multiplied by the height.

***5** (a) Take 7.69 away from 9

(b) Divide 17.6 by 0.04

6 (a) On *x* and *y* axes, each from −3 to 3, draw and label the lines $x = 2$, $x = -3$, $y = 3$ and $y = -1$.

(b) Shade the intersection of $\{(x, y) : -3 < x < 2\}$ with $\{(x, y) : -1 < y < 3\}$.

7 The wattage of a bulb is given by $W = V \times I$ where V is the voltage and I is the current in amps. Calculate the wattage of a bulb taking $\frac{1}{6}$ amp on 240 volt mains.

8 The angles of a triangle are $x°$, $2x°$ and $3x°$. Find the size of each angle.

9 (a) What different heights can be made with three bricks, each 20 cm long, 10 cm wide and 7 cm deep?

(b) Anna has a lot of sugar cubes which she finds can be built into a large cube, or spread out to make a square one layer high.

What is the smallest possible number of sugar lumps that Anna could have?

Paper 13

1 An equal number of 5p's and 10p's are worth £6. How many 5p's are there?

2 Add 12.67 to 4.9 then divide your answer by 2.

3 Juliet's age and her dad's age are in the ratio 1:4.

Juliet's dad is forty-eight. How old is Juliet?

4 Write in figures:
(a) three thousand   (b) ten thousand   (c) a million.

5 (a) Copy these sequences. Write the next two terms.
(i) 1, 4, 9, 16, ..., ...   (ii) 1, 3, 6, 10, ..., ...   (iii) 1, 1, 2, 3, ..., ...
(iv) 2, 3, 5, 7, 11, ..., ...

(b) Write the 'family name' for each sequence.

6 Simplify:

(a) $\begin{pmatrix} 3 & 4 \\ 6 & 8 \end{pmatrix} - \begin{pmatrix} 2 & 5 \\ 9 & 8 \end{pmatrix}$ (b) $\begin{pmatrix} -4 & 2 \\ 1 & -3 \end{pmatrix} + \begin{pmatrix} 7 & -1 \\ 2 & -3 \end{pmatrix}$ (c) $\begin{pmatrix} -2 & 4 & -1 \\ 1 & 6 & 3 \end{pmatrix} - \begin{pmatrix} -2 & 4 & -1 \\ -1 & -6 & -3 \end{pmatrix}$

*7 Divide £36 in the ratio 4:5. (Hint: First divide £36 into nine equal parts.)

8 Write the decimal number which is half-way between 14.65 and 20.09

9 The ratio of Adja's age to Rama's age is 5:6. If Adja is 35 years old, how old is Rama?

10 How many thousand is:
 (a) 13000   (b) 200000   (c) a million?

11 A car was hired out for £35 with fuel extra. The car used 14 litres of petrol every 100 km. Petrol cost 50p a litre and the total cost was £82.25. How many kilometres were travelled?

Paper 14

1 (a) $3008 - 173$ (b) 406×78 (c) $7371 \div 13$ (d) $1640 \div 8$

2 (a) Construct a triangle with sides of 7 cm, 6 cm and 4.5 cm.

 (b) Construct the incircle of the triangle.

 (c) By making measurements calculate the area of the triangle.

3 Write as simple common fractions (see Paper Ten):
 (a) 25%   (b) 50%   (c) 75%   (d) $33\frac{1}{3}$%   (e) 10%   (f) 15%.

4 If $x = -2$ what is the value of:
 (a) $2x$ (b) $x + 1$ (c) $x - 3$ (d) $3 + x$ (e) $3 - x$ (f) x^2?

*5 Draw a Venn diagram to illustrate:
 $X = \{1, 2, 5, 9\}$ and $Y = \{1, 3, 5, 7\}$.

6 (a) $17.091 - 3.89$ (b) $4 + 16.7 + 0.09 + 110$ (c) 40000×8300
 (d) 7.6×23800 (e) $1 \div 16$ (f) $10.01 \div 100$

7 Draw a Venn diagram to illustrate sets A and B if $n(A) = 6$, $n(B) = 4$ and $n(A \cup B) = 7$.

8 How many 8 cm by 5 cm rectangles can be cut from a 36 cm by 26 cm piece of paper? Illustrate your answer.

9 (a) In 46 B.C. Sosigenes invented the leap year. Unfortunately the extra day every four years still left each year 11 minutes 14 seconds too long. In 325 A.D. the accumulated error was corrected by missing out the nearest whole number of days. How many days were missed out?

 (b) What system is now used to avoid the error in the length of a year building up so quickly? What error is there in the new system?

Paper 15

1 What is the change from £5 if I spend: (a) £1.76   (b) £4.08   (c) £3.52?

2 (a) $-6-9$ (b) $-6+9$ (c) $6-9$ (d) -7×8 (e) -7×-8
    (f) $16\div-2$ (g) $-16\div2$ (h) $4--3$ (i) $1+-1$ (j) $-5--3$

3 (a) Calculate the perimeter and the area of Figure P25.

    (b) Calculate the area of Figure P26.

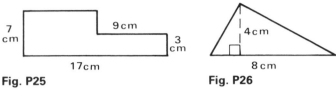

Fig. P25   **Fig. P26**

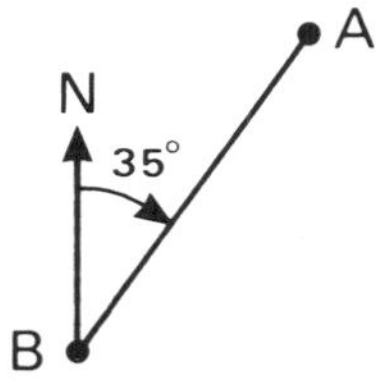

Fig. P27

4 **Example** In Figure P27 the bearing of A from B is 035°.

State the bearing of A from B for each diagram in Figure P28.

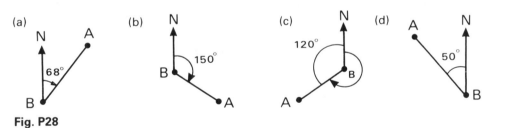

Fig. P28

*5 Draw the following journey to a scale of 1 cm represents 10 km:

Start from P on a bearing of 180°. After 30 km turn to 090° for 80 km, then turn to 000° for 30 km. Finally turn to 270° for 80 km.

6 John and Carol have saved £500. Carol has saved £20 more than John. How much has John saved?

7 Calculate the area of Figure P29.

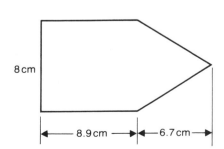

Fig. P29

8 (a) To a scale of 1:100000 how many cm represent 100000 cm?

(b) How many centimetres make one kilometre?

(c) To a scale of 1:100000 draw a plan of a journey from A to B via M where A to M is 7 km, M to B is 3 km, M is on a bearing of 110° from A, and B is due east of M.

(d) How far is A from B to the nearest 0.1 km?

Paper 16

1 Write as a percentage: (a) $\frac{1}{4}$ (b) $\frac{4}{5}$ (c) $\frac{3}{25}$ (d) $\frac{7}{20}$.

2 How many:
(a) mm in 5 cm   (b) ml in 5 cl   (c) metres in 1 km   (d) cm in 3.6 m?

3 Find (a) to (e) in the table.

Time	1 h	1 h	1 h	(c)	$\frac{1}{2}$ h	$\frac{1}{2}$ h
Distance	30 miles	70 miles	(b)	100 miles	20 miles	(e)
Speed	30 m.p.h.	(a)	80 m.p.h.	50 m.p.h.	(d)	60 m.p.h.

*4 In Figure P30 calculate the angles *a*, *b* and *c* then write the special name of each triangle.

(a)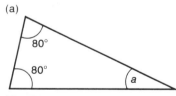

(b)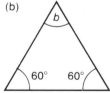

(c)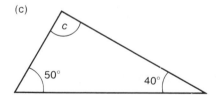

Fig. P30

*5 Two angles of a triangle are each 66°. What is the size of the third angle?

*6 (a) $-7-2$ (b) $6--3$ (c) -2×-4 (d) $12\div-4$ (e) $-12\div-4$

*7 Follow the construction shown in Figure P31 to find O, the centre of the circumcircle of triangle ABC. Make BC = 8 cm, AB = 6 cm and AC = 5 cm.

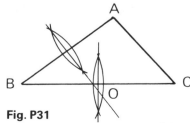

Fig. P31

8 A triangle has two equal angles, with the third angle twice as large. Find the size of each angle and say what kind of triangle it is.

9 How many 5 ml medicine doses can be taken from a 20 cl bottle?

10 If $a = -5$ and $b = -2$ find the value of:
(a) a^2 (b) ab (c) $a + b$ (d) $a - b$ (e) $b - a$.

11 Rewrite in alphabetical order: $b - 2d + a - 2c + e$.

12 A brick 20 cm by 18 cm by 12 cm weighs 1 kg. What will a brick of the same material weigh if it is:
(a) 40 cm by 18 cm by 12 cm (b) 40 cm by 36 cm by 12 cm
(c) 40 cm by 36 cm by 24 cm (d) 10 cm by 36 cm by 12 cm?

13 A brick weighs a pound plus half a brick. What does a brick and a half weigh?

Paper 17

1 Change to a simplified fraction (see Paper 10):
(a) 12% (b) 35% (c) 105%.

2 Ana has 18 coins. Jim's to Ana's coins are in the ratio 3:1. How many coins has Jim?

3 Draw a diagram to show that a quarter of a half is an eighth.

4 Write correct to the nearest hundred:
(a) 742 (b) 893 (c) 992 (d) 1006.

5 (a) $\dfrac{14 \times 15}{5}$ (b) $\dfrac{3 \times 14}{7}$ (c) $\dfrac{2 \times 7}{16}$

6 If possible, draw a quadrilateral with four equal sides but no right-angled corners.

7 In trials, a die came up six 756 times in 1000 throws. Write a few sentences about this result.

8 On a map 1 cm represents 100 km. What length is represented by: (a) 1 mm (b) 3 mm?

*9 (a) $3001 - 455$ (b) 706×87 (c) 70.6×8.7 (see part (b))
    (d) $7.6 - 4.85$ (e) $15.3 \div 0.03$

10 (a) Draw a plan showing two beacons 5 km apart with B north-west of A, to a scale of 1 cm represents 1 km.

    (b) State the bearing of B from A as a 3-figure bearing.

    (c) Find the bearing of A from B as both a cardinal and a 3-figure bearing.

11 What number squared is the same as twice the number?

12 In olden days the silver coins were sixpence (6d), shilling (12d or 1/-), florin (24d or 2/-) and half-a-crown (30d or 2/6).

Coins of the same value had the same weight, e.g. two shillings and one sixpence weighed the same as half-a-crown.

There were 240d in £1.

    (a) In £1 how many: (i) sixpences   (ii) shillings   (iii) florins   (iv) half-crowns?

    (b) Write five possible numbers of coins in a bag containing 30d in silver.

    (c) How many half-crowns weigh the same as 1 florin, 3 shillings and 5 sixpences?

Paper 18

1 John says it is 3 miles to school, to the nearest mile. What is the furthest that John could be from school?

2 Simplify by cancelling: (a) $\dfrac{5}{20}$ (b) $\dfrac{16}{24}$ (c) $\dfrac{350}{500}$.

3 For Figure P32:

    (a) Write the equation of:
       (i) the x-axis   (ii) the y-axis
       (iii) line m (iv) line n (v) line p

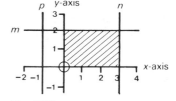

    (b) Write the co-ordinates of the intersection of lines m and p.

    (c) Copy and complete the following description of the hatched region:
       $\{(x, y): \;\; <x< \;\; ; \;\; <y< \;\; \}$

Fig. P32

4   Example $\frac{3}{7} = \frac{9}{21}$ (both 3 and 7 have been multiplied by 3)

Copy and complete:
(a) $\frac{2}{7} = \frac{}{21}$ (b) $\frac{3}{4} = \frac{}{12}$ (c) $\frac{4}{5} = \frac{}{20}$ (d) $\frac{3}{8} = \frac{}{16}$

*5 (a) $\frac{4}{7} + \frac{1}{3}$ (Change both to 21 at the bottom.)

(b) $\frac{3}{5} + \frac{1}{3}$ (Change both to fifteenths.)

(c) $\frac{1}{8} + \frac{3}{4}$

6 (a) $\frac{3}{8} + \frac{3}{4}$ (b) $\frac{4}{7} - \frac{1}{3}$

7 Find three-quarters of: (a) 12   (b) 100   (c) 64   (d) 10.

8 Write the following in full, replacing the stars with the correct digits.

(a) $** \times 23 = *9*5$ (b) $*** \times 37 = 3*3*7$

9 **Example** $169.2 \div 36 \xrightarrow{\text{divide each by 4}} 42.3 \div 9 = 4.7$

'Avoid' long-division in a similar manner to find:
(a) $55.2 \div 24$ (b) $371 \div 35$ (c) $11.34 \div 1.8$

10 An old frog can only jump half as far as he has just jumped. If he has just jumped 1 metre, what is the furthest he can possibly go from where he is now?

Paper 19

1 (a) $3.65 - 2.97$ (b) 7.7×7.7 (c) $1\frac{5}{8} + 3\frac{3}{4}$ (d) $4\frac{2}{3} - 2\frac{2}{5}$
(e) 31.6×1000

2 Find the value of c if:
(a) $c + 18 = 27$ (b) $15 - c = 9$ (c) $5c = 35$ (d) $7c = 56$ (e) $9c = 63$
(f) $c - 7 = -4$.

3 List the set of factors of: (a) 30   (b) 42.

4 (a) $305 \div 0.5$ (b) $4.28 \div 0.8$ (c) Write one-third of a hundred as a mixed number.

5 (a) $-2 - 8$ (b) -3×-4 (c) $-7 + 1$ (d) $-5 \div -5$ (e) $2 - -3$

*6 If $h = 5$ state the value of: (a) $2h$ (b) h^2 (c) $3h + 1$.

*7 Are the following pairs of sets disjoint, or intersecting, or is one a subset of the other?
(a) $A = \{2, 5\}$; $B = \{3\}$ (b) $C = \{8, 3\}$; $D = \{8\}$ (c) $E = \{4, 5\}$; $F = \{5, 6\}$

*8 For the sets in question 7 list:
(a) $C \cup D$ (b) $C \cap D$ (c) $E \cup F$ (d) $E \cap F$.

*9 Calculate the area of the triangle in Figure P33 by making suitable measurements.

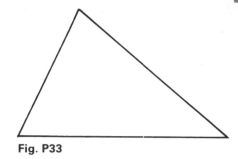

Fig. P33

*10 Share £48.07 equally between 23 people. How much each?

11 Figure P34 shows Suki's pencil partly hidden by her rubber.

On the left of the rubber $\frac{2}{5}$ of the pencil can be seen whilst $\frac{1}{5}$ of it can be seen on the right. How long is the pencil?

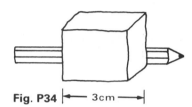

Fig. P34 |← 3cm →|

12 How many days from 29 August 1995 to 2 July 1996 inclusive?

13 1 apple and 3 oranges cost 40p whilst 2 apples and 4 oranges cost 58p.

What will 3 apples and 3 oranges cost?

14 A cube has each face painted a different colour. In how many ways can it be placed on a table so that the colours are in different positions?

15 Figure P35 shows an accurate copy of a watch face. What time is the watch showing?

Fig. P35

Paper 20

1 Using compasses, ruler and pencil only, construct an angle of:
(a) 60° (b) 30° (c) 90°.

2 How many lines of symmetry has:
(a) an equilateral triangle (b) a square (c) an isosceles triangle (d) a kite
(e) a rhombus (f) a parallelogram?

3 A quadrilateral has three equal angles of 100°. What is the size of the fourth angle?

P

*4 Every 25 minutes a bus leaves Newtown for Garden City.

    If a bus leaves at 1130, write the 24-hour-clock times of the next five buses.

*5 Copy and complete the route matrix for the one-way network shown in Figure P36.

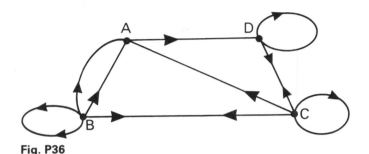

		To			
		A	B	C	D
F r o m	A	0			
	B	2			
	C	1			
	D	0	0	1	1

Fig. P36

*6 (a) 0.36×10 (b) 0.36×100 (c) 0.36×1000 (d) $0.36 \div 10$
    (e) $5.71 \div 100$ (f) 100×1000 (g) 300×500 (h) 400×5000

*7 Write all the facts you can about the diagonals of: (a) a square   (b) a rhombus.

8 (a) Construct accurately a square of side 6 cm, using compasses for the 90° angle.

    (b) Show on your square all its lines of symmetry.

9 Each of the buses on the timetable takes the same time between each town.

    Copy and complete the table.

Alford	0845	1015	1305
Camtown	0901		
Lowham	0944		

10 Write as a decimal of a metre:
    (a) 38 cm   (b) 8 cm   (c) 102 cm   (d) 32 mm   (e) 105 mm.

11 If $x = 2.305$, $y = 2000$ and $z = 0.079$ show all necessary working to find:
    (a) $x + y + z$ (b) $y - x$ (c) xy (d) yz (e) xz (f) $z \div y$.

12 A man wishes to average 60 m.p.h. on a journey, but half-way there he finds he has only averaged 30 m.p.h.

    What speed must he average for the rest of the journey if he is to arrive on time?

Paper 21

1 $A = \{169.48, 1208.755, 96.095, 1008.999\}$

Rewrite the elements of set A rounded:
(a) to the nearest hundred   (b) to the nearest unit   (c) to 2 decimal places.

2 By rounding to one-figure accuracy find an approximate answer to the following.

Example $764 \times 79 \simeq 800 \times 80 = 64\,000$

(a) 417×28 (b) 7631×44 (c) 3218×553

3 Find n if:
(a) $2n = 15$ (b) $3n - 1 = 14$ (c) $\frac{n}{2} = 20$ (d) $\frac{n}{2} + 1 = 5$.

4 Name all the **parallelograms** with:
(a) right angles   (b) equal diagonals   (c) obtuse angles
(d) diagonals crossing at right angles.

5 Which of the special quadrilaterals at the start of exercise 22A have one, and only one, axis of symmetry?

6 Construct a triangle with sides 6 cm, 5 cm and 5 cm, together with its circumcircle. (See Paper Sixteen, question 7.)

*7 Copy the axes shown in Figure P37. (There is no need to use squared paper.)

(a) Draw and label the lines:
   (i) $x = 2$ (ii) $y = 3$.

(b) Hatch the region $\{(x, y) : 0 < x < 2; 0 < y < 3\}$.

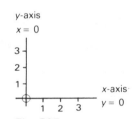

Fig. P37

8 Tara has x pence and Robin has 56 pence. If Tara had twice as much they would have £1 altogether. How much has Tara?

9 Draw the one-way network for the route matrix, positioning the nodes as shown.

		To		
		A	B	C
F	A	2	1	1
r o m	B	0	0	2
	C	0	1	1

A   B   C

207

10 Draw axes from -6 to 6 each. By choosing suitable values for x and y draw graphs of the equations:
(a) $y = x$ (b) $y = x + 1$ (c) $y = x - 1$ (d) $y = -x$.

11 Would you rather have half a kilogram of 10p's or a kilogram of 5p's? Why?

Paper 22

1   (a) $\frac{3}{5} + \frac{1}{3}$ (Change both to fifteenths.)   (b) $2\frac{3}{5} - 1\frac{1}{3}$ (c) $16 \times \frac{5}{12}$ (d) $3\frac{1}{3} - 2\frac{3}{5}$

2   (a) $7 + 2 - 3$ (b) $7 - 2 + 3$ (c) $7 - 2 - 3$ (d) $-7 + 2 + 3$ (e) $-7 - 2 - 3$

3   (a) 7×-8 (b) -7×-8 (c) $63 \div 9$ (d) $63 \div -9$ (e) $-63 \div -9$

*4   If $a = 2$ what is:
(a) a^2 (b) $3a$ (c) $2a$ (d) a^3 (or $a \times a \times a$)?

*5   If $b = -2$ what is:
(a) b^2 (b) $b - 1$ (c) $b + 1$ (d) $1 - b$?

*6   How long will a journey of 100 miles take at an average speed of 40 miles per hour?

*7   A car travels 8 miles on a litre of petrol. How many litres will it use in 100 miles?

*8   Write each of the vectors $\underset{\sim}{b}$ to $\underset{\sim}{f}$ in Figure P38 as a column matrix.

Example $\underset{\sim}{a} = \begin{pmatrix} -3 \\ 2 \end{pmatrix}$

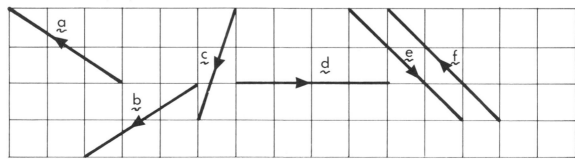

Fig. P38

9   If $k = 5$, $t = 9$ and $m = 11$ find the value of:
(a) $k + t + 3m$ (b) $2k + 3t + m$ (c) $4k + t - m$ (d) $8k - t - m$
(e) $7t - m - k$ (f) $\dfrac{t}{k}$ (g) $\dfrac{2m + k}{t}$.

10 (a) A train travelling at 60 km/h takes 6 seconds to pass a signal. How long is the train?
(b) Two trains of equal length, both travelling at 60 km/h, take 6 seconds to pass each other. How long are the trains?

11 How many shapes can five squares make if each square must have at least one side completely touching the complete side of another, and shapes are counted as the same if they look alike when reflected or rotated?

Paper 23

1   To where does the point (1, 2) move when it is translated by the vector $\begin{pmatrix} 3 \\ 0 \end{pmatrix}$?

2   Four books cost £5. What will six of the same books cost?

3   Eight fence panels cost £68. What will six cost?

4   A spring increases by 30 mm with a 5 kg load. What is the increase for 8 kg?

*5 The table shows the VAT at 15% to add to the price of an article.

Price	20p	40p	£1	£2	£5	£10	£20	£50	£100
VAT (15%)	3p	6p	15p	30p	75p	£1.50	£3	£7.50	£15

Example   To find the VAT on an article of price £1.20
From the table, the VAT on £1 is 15p and the VAT on 20p is 3p. Total VAT = 18p.

Find the VAT on an article of price:
(a) £5.20   (b) £1.40   (c) £7   (d) £25   (e) £55   (f) £102
(g) £102.40   (h) £10.60   (i) £21.60

*6 For Figure P39:

(a) Write as column matrices the vectors a, b and c.

(b) If each square was 1 cm² what would be the area of the triangle?

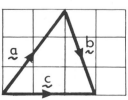

Fig. P39

209

7 (a) Draw axes, each from −5 to 5, on 1 cm-squared paper.

(b) Starting from (− 3, 3) draw the following vectors, each starting from the end of the previous one.

$$\binom{5}{2}; \quad \binom{2}{-5}; \quad \binom{-5}{-2}; \quad \binom{-2}{5}.$$

(c) On the same grid, use the square with its vertices at (− 3, 5), (4, 5), (4, − 2) and (− 3, − 2), and the area of a triangle formula, to find the area of the square drawn in part (b).

8 In the sum shown, A, B, C and D are four consecutive digits. The third row is made up of the same four digits. Write the complete sum in figures.

```
        A   B   C   D
        D   C   B   A
        *   *   *   *    +
      ─────────────────
      1   2   3   0   0
```

Paper 24

1 Approximate to the nearest hundred:
(a) 4826   (b) 381   (c) 42094   (d) 6163   (e) 81001   (f) 90199.

2 Using the Tariff in exercise 27C copy and complete the following bill for a party of six adults, fourteen children aged 14 years and ten children aged 13 years.

They are all taking bicycles.

The party will land at Calais (France) and return from Ostend (Belgium).

NAME Carr Youth Club	OUT: *Standard*	RETURN: *Summer weekend*

3 (a) Draw and label axes from 0 to 5.

(b) Hatch /// the region $\{(x, y):1 < x < 4\}$.   (c) Hatch \\\ the region $\{(x, y):3 < y < 5\}$

(d) Draw a similar set of axes and shade the intersection of the regions $\{(x, y): 1 < x < 4\}$ and $\{(x, y): 3 < y < 5\}$.

*4 (a) List the elements of the following sets:
$A = \{$months with 31 days$\}$; $B = \{$months with 30 days$\}$.

(b) What is: (i) n(A)   (ii) n(B)?

(c) Which month does not belong to set A or B? How many days has it?

5 Draw a Venn diagram of the correct type (intersecting, subset or disjoint) and write the correct number of elements in each section if:

(a) n(A) = 6; n(B) = 4; n($A \cap B$) = 4

(b) n(C) = 2; n(D) = 5; n($C \cup D$) = 6

(c) n(E) = 8; n(F) = 9; n($E \cup F$) = 17.

6 List the following sets of integers:
(a) $\{n: 2 < n < 6\}$ (b) $\{n: 1 < n \leqslant 5\}$.

7 Gomez, Ali, June and Rene pay for a block of lottery tickets in the ratio 20:12:15:13.

(a) What fraction of the cost does each pay, as simply as possible?

(b) If they win £9000 how much should each receive?

Paper 25

1 (a) If the rate of exchange stands at £1 = DM4.10, how many DM would you receive for £200?

(b) If the rate changed to £1 = DM4.26, how much *more* would you receive?

2 Add together:
(a) -3 and -4 (b) -2 and 3   (c) 4 and -6 (d) 17 and 5
(e) -17 and 9   (f) -8 and -7.

3 Ahmad has to travel 220 miles. He plans to average 45 m.p.h. and needs to arrive by 6 p.m. About when should he set out, allowing half-an-hour for a refreshment stop?

4 Round correct to one decimal place: (a) 1.624   (b) 3.729   (c) 8.578

5 Round the numbers in question 4 correct to two decimal places.

*6 Solve:
(a) $7 + a = 4$ (b) $a + 8 = 3$ (c) $7 - a = 4$ (d) $3a + 2 = 8$ (e) $5a + 12 = 62$.

7 Draw a graph, as in exercise 11B, for the mapping:

(a) $x \rightarrow x + 2$, where $-3 \leqslant x \leqslant 3$

(b) $x \rightarrow x - 2$, where $0 \leqslant x \leqslant 2$

(c) $x \rightarrow 2x$, where $-1 \leqslant x \leqslant 1$.

8 The Braille alphabet is made up of six raised dots positioned as shown.

```
1 . . 4
2 . . 5
3 . . 6
```

A to J are represented by dots 1, 2, 4 and 5 as follows.

A is 1 (⠁);   B is 1, 2 (⠃);   C is 1, 4;   D is 1, 4, 5;   E is 1, 5;   F is 1, 2, 4;
G is 1, 2, 4, 5;   H is 1, 2, 5;   I is 2, 4;   J is 2, 4, 5.

K to T are formed by adding dot 3 to A to J.
U to Z are formed by adding dot 6 to K to O, except for W, which is 2, 4, 5, 6.

Draw the Braille alphabet. You might like to try to learn it.

You could also work out how many different dot patterns are possible. Do they all **feel** different? How many more usable dot patterns are there besides the 26 used for letters? Are these used for Braille? If so, for what?

Paper 26

1 In Figure P40, point A is NW (north-west) of B.

(a) What is the cardinal bearing of B from A?

(b) What is the 3-figure bearing of:
  (i) A from B   (ii) B from A?

Fig. P40

2 Increase:
(a) £1 by 10%   (b) £20 by 10%   (c) £15 by 5%.

3 Decrease:
(a) £1 by 8%   (b) £1 by 4%   (c) £100 by 9%.

4 Copy each Venn diagram in Figure P41 twice.

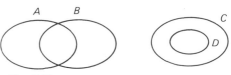

Shade the region:
(a) A ∪ B   (b) A ∩ B   (c) C ∩ D   (d) C ∪ D.   **Fig. P41**

*5 State with reasons the size of each lettered angle in Figure P42.

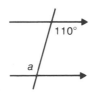   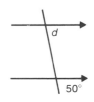

Fig. P42

6 Draw and label four sets of axes from − 3 to 3 each.

Answering one part on each grid hatch the region:
(a) $x > 2$ (b) $y < 2$ (c) $x > -1$ (d) $y < -1$.

7 A shop decreases its prices by 4%. What will be the new price for:
(a) a £54 coat   (b) a £24 skirt   (c) a £16 shirt   (d) a £22 pair of trousers
(e) a £48 jacket?

8 Calculate with reasons the values of angles a, b, c and d in Figure P43.

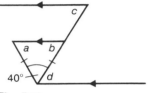

Fig. P43

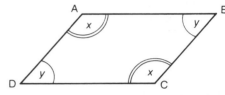

Fig. P44

9 Prove that, in Figure P44, AB and BC must be parallel to DC and AD respectively.

Paper 27

1 If $A = \{1, 2, 3, 4, 5, 6, 7\}$ and $B = \{2, 4, 6, 8, 10, 12\}$, are the following true or false?
(a) $2 \in (A \cap B)$ (b) $\{1, 2, 8\} \subset A$ (c) $\{2, 4, 6\} \not\subset B$ (d) $A \supset \{3, 4, 5\}$ (e) $n(A \cup B) = 13$

2 Copy and complete:
(a) $1\,km = \ldots m$ (b) $100\,mm = \ldots cm$ (c) $1\,m = \ldots cm$
(d) $1\,m^2 = \ldots cm^2$ (*not* 100)   (e) 1 litre $= \ldots cm^3$ (f) $1000\,g = \ldots kg$
(g) $6\,kg = \ldots g$ (h) $5000\,m = \ldots km$ (i) 1 tonne $= \ldots kg$ (j) 1 hectare $= \ldots m^2$.

*3 For the Venn diagrams in Figure P45 list:
(a) the six sets A to F (b) $A \cap B$ (c) $C \cap D$ (d) $E \cap F$ (e) $A \cup B$
(f) $C \cup D$ (g) $E \cup F$.

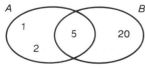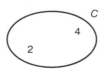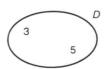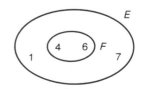

Fig. P45

213

P

*4 Calculate the fourth angle in each quadrilateral shown in Figure P46.

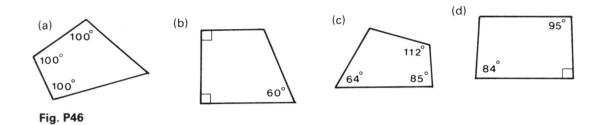

Fig. P46

5 Calculate, showing all working: (a) $1.413 \div 0.9$ (b) $0.036 \div 0.6$ (c) $46.9 \div 0.07$

6 Copy and complete:
(a) 1.4 litres $= \ldots$ cm^3 (b) 4.15 tonnes $= \ldots$ kg (c) 520 cm$^3 = \ldots$ litres.

7 (a) Two angles of a quadrilateral are $70°$ and $112°$. The other angles are equal; how many degrees is each?

(b) The angles of a quadrilateral are $90°$, $x°$, $2x°$ and $3x°$. Find the value of x.

8 A washing powder consists of two chemicals, A and B, in the ratio $2:5$. Chemical A costs 0.1p per gram and chemical B costs 0.06p per gram.

(a) How many grams of A in a 0.840 kg box of washing powder?

(b) What is the cost of the chemicals in the box?

9 Convert: (a) 6 g/cm^3 to kg/litre (b) 50 km/h to m/s.

Paper 28

1 Find for 4, 5, 4, 7, 6, 9, 3, 8, 7, 4: (a) the mean (b) the mode (c) the median.

2 State, with a reason, the size of each lettered angle in Figure P47.

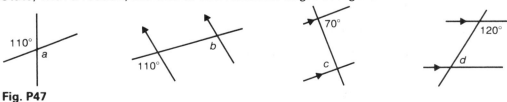

Fig. P47

3 $A = \begin{pmatrix} 2 & 4 \\ -7 & 6 \end{pmatrix}$; $B = \begin{pmatrix} 3 & -2 \\ 6 & -4 \end{pmatrix}$; $C = \begin{pmatrix} 0 & -4 \\ -2 & 3 \end{pmatrix}$

Find: (a) $A + B$ (b) $A + C$ (c) $B + C$ (d) $A - B$ (e) $A - C$ (f) $B - C$.

4 (a) $-20 \div 4$ (b) $-18 \div -3$ (c) 6×-4 (d) -7×3 (e) -7×-4

*5 How many degrees, measured clockwise, between:
(a) N and E (b) N and NE (c) N and SE (d) E and NW (e) W and SE?

*6 Taking π as 3.1 find the circumference of a circle with:
(a) diameter 4 cm (b) radius 6 cm.

*7 (a) $6 - 1\frac{1}{2}$ (b) $8 - \frac{3}{4}$ (c) $4\frac{1}{2} + 3\frac{3}{4}$ (d) $4\frac{1}{2} - \frac{3}{4}$ (e) 7.6×0.8 (f) $7.6 \div 0.8$

8 (a) $4 - \frac{3}{5}$ (b) $7 - \frac{8}{9}$ (c) $6\frac{1}{4} + 3\frac{2}{3}$ (d) $4\frac{1}{3} - 3\frac{1}{5}$ (e) $6\frac{2}{3} - \frac{4}{5}$ (f) $4\frac{1}{8} - 2\frac{3}{4}$

9 Solve:
(a) $c - 3 = -2$ (b) $d + 6 = -8$ (c) $3g + 3 = 15$ (d) $2h - 4 = 8$
(e) $3j + 4 = 1$ (f) $8k - 9 = 7$.

10 Draw accurately a set of squares with sides from 2 cm to 8 cm at 1 cm intervals.

Measure the diagonal of each, then calculate perimeter ÷ diagonal. Comment on your results.

Paper 29

1 Calculate:
(a) $9 - 7 + 5$ (b) $9 - 4 - 6$ (c) $-4 + 1 + 6$ (d) $-4 - 5 - 3$
(e) $4 - 6 + 3 - 7$ (f) $8 - 9 + 7 - 6$ (g) $8 - 5 - 7 + 2$.

2 Find: (a) 5% of £1 (b) 6% of £10 (c) 9% of £15.

*3 Calculate the selling price of an article if:
(a) the cost price is £10 and the profit is £1.50
(b) the cost price is £12 and a loss of £1.04 is made
(c) the cost price is £24.32 and a loss of 87p is made.

*4 Solve: (a) $2x + 3 = 9$ (b) $4x + 2 = 12$ (c) $4x - 7 = 13$.

*5 Copy and complete: (a) $\frac{3}{4} = \frac{6}{}$ (b) $\frac{7}{8} = \frac{}{16}$ (c) $\frac{3}{7} = \frac{}{28}$ (d) $\frac{3}{5} = \frac{9}{}$

*6 Copy Figure P48, using 2 cm and 4 cm radii arcs.

Fig. P48

7 If each diagram in Figure P49 is the base of a 9 cm high prism, calculate the volume of each prism.

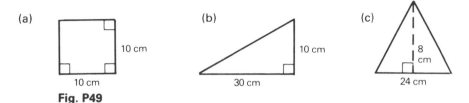

(a) 10 cm, 10 cm

(b) 10 cm, 30 cm

(c) 8 cm, 24 cm

Fig. P49

8 What is the capacity of each prism in question 7 in litres?

9 (a) Construct a triangle with sides of 5 cm, 5 cm and 6 cm.

(b) Bisect each angle and draw the incircle.

(c) Construct the triangle again, but this time construct the perpendicular bisectors of the sides and draw the circumcircle.

10 Using either up-to-date exchange rates given to you by your teacher, or those given in exercise 27A, say about how much the Sterling equivalent is of:
(a) FB 1650   (b) Fs 110.49   (c) DKr 478.72   (d) OS 1343.86   (e) Pta 7623.75

Paper 30

1 In Figure P50 each pair of shapes is similar. The ratio of the lengths is given and the units are metres. Find (a) to (k).

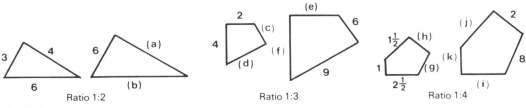

Ratio 1:2   Ratio 1:3   Ratio 1:4

Fig. P50

2 In Figure P51 what is:
(a) n(*F*) (b) n(*R*) (c) n(*F* ∩ *R*)
(d) n(*F* ∪ *R*)?

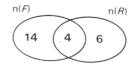

Fig. P51

*3 Aziz has £6.84, Karen has £1.71, and Samir has £0.87.

(a) How much have they altogether? (b) How much more has Karen than Samir?

(c) What is the difference between Aziz's amount and Samir's amount?

(d) If Karen gave a third of her money to Samir how much would each then have?

(e) If the friends share their money out equally how much would each have?

*4 Calculate the areas of the shapes in Figure P52. Units are centimetres.

(a)
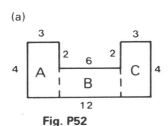
Fig. P52

(b)
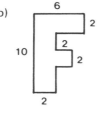

(c)
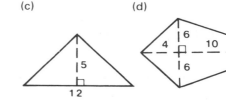

(d)

5 (a) $1\frac{3}{4} + 2\frac{1}{5}$ (b) $3\frac{1}{4} + 2\frac{5}{6}$ (c) $3\frac{7}{8} - 2\frac{1}{4}$ (d) $4\frac{3}{8} - 2\frac{1}{2}$ (e) $3\frac{1}{5} - 2\frac{1}{4}$ (f) $\frac{3}{5} \times 15$

6 The following statements tell you something about the order of four letters, A, B, C and D. Each statement is either completely true or completely false. What is the order of the letters?
 (i) A is next to B; C is next to D. (ii) B is next to C; A is on the left of C.
(iii) A is next to C; B is on the left of C. (iv) A is on the left of D; B is on the left of A.

7 For saving her life a lady offered to pay her rescuer either £1000 or else 1p that year, then 2p the next, 4p the next, 8p the next, and so on, doubling the amount each year.

Discuss which would be the better choice.

Glossary

If you cannot remember what a word means, or cannot find a particular topic in the book, this glossary should help you.

Note

When you are told to 'see BEARINGS (1)', for example, look up the heading Bearings in the Summaries of Book 2 (pages 230 to 234), and look in chapter 1 of this book for more information.

When you are told to 'see CIRCLES' for example, with no chapter number, this refers you to the heading Circles in the Summaries of Book 1 (pages 223 to 229).

Words in italics, like *digit*, may themselves be looked up in the glossary.

A

Acute	An angle between 0° and 90°.
Adjacent	'Next to', as in 'adjacent angles': see STRAIGHT-LINE ANGLES (28)
Arc	Part of a circle: see CIRCLES
	Part of a network: see NETWORKS

B

Bar-chart	A diagram to show information by a series of columns or bars.
Bearing	The direction of one object from another: see BEARINGS (1)
Binary	The simplest possible number system, using only the *digits* 0 and 1.

C

Cardinal	The cardinal points are north, south, west and east. Cardinal bearings are stated with reference to these. Half way between S and E is SE; half way between E and SE is ESE, etc. See BEARINGS (1)
Chord	Part of a circle: see CIRCLES
Column matrix	A *matrix* which consists of only one upright column of figures. A *vector* is a column matrix. See exercise 6B.
Concave	'With a cave'; a concave *polygon* has at least one angle pointing inwards ('re-entrant'). See POLYGONS
Consecutive	Following one after another; 4, 5, 6, 7 are consecutive *integers*.
Construct	Draw accurately, usually using only a ruler and a pair of compasses.
Convex	'Pointing outwards'; the opposite of *concave*. See POLYGONS
Co-ordinate	The method of fixing the position of a point on a grid; also called an Ordered Pair. See GRAPHS
Cube	Shape: a solid with six square faces.
	Algebra: a number or letter multiplied by itself, then by itself again; written as k^3.
Cubic	One cubic centimetre (1 cm^3) is the volume of a cube of side 1 cm. It is also the volume of anything with the same volume as this cube. 1 cm^3 is the same volume as 1 millilitre (1 ml).

D

Denary	'Based on ten'; the usual number system. See BINARY ARITHMETIC (19)
Denominator	The correct name for the bottom number in a fraction. It 'denominates' (names) the kind of fraction that it is, e.g. the 4 in $\frac{3}{4}$ tells you that the fraction is of quarters (or fourths).
Diameter	Part of a circle: see CIRCLES
Difference	The result of a subtraction.
Digit	One of the figures 0, 1, 2, 3, 4, 5, 6, 7, 8, and 9.
Digit-sum	Used in this book for the result of continually adding the *digits* of a number until a single digit results, e.g. the digit-sum of 156 is 3. See DIVISIBILITY
Disjoint	'Not connected'; disjoint sets have no common *elements*. See exercise 4C.
Domain	The set of numbers, or the *region* from which you start. See MAPPINGS

E

Element	A member of a set. See SETS
Equilateral	Equal sided. See TRIANGLES

F

Face	A flat side of a solid.
Factor	An *integer* that divides exactly into another integer; e.g. the factors of 12 are 1, 2, 3, 4, 6, and 12.
Figure	A diagram, or a *digit*.
Frequency	How often something happens.

H

Hexadecimal	'Base sixteen'; it uses sixteen digits, the usual 0 to 9, then A to F for ten to fifteen. Hexadecimal is the usual system used to convey information to a computer, called 'machine code'.
Hypotenuse	The longest side of a right-angled triangle; it is always opposite the right angle. See PYTHAGORAS' THEOREM (18)

I

Image	The result of transforming an *object*, e.g. by *translating* or reflecting it. Also the result of a *mapping*, e.g. under the mapping $y \to 2y$, the image of 6 is 12.
Improper fraction	A top-heavy fraction, like $\frac{13}{2}$. *Mixed numbers* must be changed to improper fractions before being multiplied or divided.
Inclusive	'Including both ends', e.g. {*integers* from 1 to 3 inclusive} = {1, 2, 3}.
Index/Indices	The raised figure/figures that give the *power*, e.g. the 2 in x^2.
Infinite	Without ending.
Integer	A *whole number*, like -4 or 18.
Intersecting	'Crossing each other'; Intersecting sets: see exercise 4C.
Isosceles	With two equal sides. See TRIANGLES Isosceles trapezium: see exercise 22A.

L

Litre	The metric unit of capacity (e.g. for liquids). See METRIC SYSTEM
Locus	The path made by a moving point. See exercises 8B and 8C.

M

Mapping	See MAPPINGS
Matrix	A table of figures. See MATRIX ADDITION (6)
Mean	The correct statistical term for what most people refer to as 'the average'. See MEAN
Median	The middle of an ordered set of data. See exercise 32B.
Mixed number	Consisting of partly an integer and partly a common fraction, e.g. $3\frac{3}{4}$.
Mode	The most frequent item in a set of data. See exercise 32A.
Multiple	A number made by multiplying one *integer* by another, e.g. 16 and 48 are multiples of 8.

N

Natural number	A number used to count objects, that is, a positive *integer*.
Network	A diagram of connected lines. See NETWORKS
Node	A junction of *arcs* in a *network*. See NETWORKS
Null set	A set with no elements, represented by $\emptyset$ or { }.
Numerator	The top number in a fraction. It tells you how many of that kind of fraction there are, e.g. the 3 in $\frac{3}{4}$ tells you that there are 3 quarters.

O

Object	The point or shape that is being transformed, e.g. by a reflection or *translation*. Also the number that is going to be mapped by a *mapping*.
Obtuse	An angle between 90° and 180°.
Octal	'Base eight'; using the digits 0 to 7 only.
Ordered pair	Another name for the *co-ordinates* of a point.
Origin	The point (0, 0) on a graph. See GRAPHS

P

Pentagon	A five-sided shape. Not to be confused with *polygon*.
Perimeter	The boundary of an object; the perimeter of a circle is called its *circumference*.
Perpendicular bisector	A line which cuts another in half at right angles. See exercise 8C.
Pictogram	A chart showing information by means of picture symbols that represent a certain amount.
Pie-chart	A chart showing information by dividing up a circle.
Polygon	A many-sided figure; see POLYGONS
Power	The result of multiplying a number by itself a number of times, e.g. '5 raised to the power 3' is $5 \times 5 \times 5 = 125$. It can also be shown by an *index*, e.g. 5^3.

Prime number	A number with only two *factors*, 1 and itself. 2, 13 and 29 are prime numbers, but 1, 9 and 51 are not.
Prism	A solid with the same shape (its 'cross-section') all through it. See exercises 33A and 33B.
Product	The result of a multiplication.

Q

Quadrilateral	A four-sided *polygon*.
Quotient	The result of a division.

R

Radius	Part of a circle: see CIRCLES
Range	See MAPPINGS
Ratio	A comparison between two amounts, usually written with 'to' or a colon (:), e.g. the ratio of boys to girls at a party was 3:4. See RATIO/SCALES. See PROPORTION (26) and SIMILAR SHAPES (34)
Rectangular numbers	*Integers* which are not prime, except the number 1. They can be arranged as a rectangle of dots.
Recur	To repeat, as in recurring decimals, e.g. 0.333333333... The recurring figure is shown with a dot (or two dots), as in 0.$\overset{.}{3}$ for 0.333... and 0.1$\overset{.}{4}$5$\overset{.}{3}$ for 0.1453453453...
Reflex	An angle greater than 180°. In geometry, 'angle ABC' is taken to be the acute or obtuse angle between the lines AB and BC. If the reflex angle is meant then we write 'angle ABC reflex'.
Region	A special area of a diagram, especially of a graph or *network*. See NETWORKS. See GRAPHS (13)
Regular	Having both equal sides and equal angles, e.g. a regular *quadrilateral* is a square.

S

Similar	Two shapes are similar if one is a mathematical enlargement of the other. See SIMILAR SHAPES (34)
Square	Algebra: a letter with *index* 2, like x^2. Number: an *integer* that is made by multiplying another integer by itself.
Standard form	The method of writing a number as a number between 1 and 10 multiplied by a *power* of ten, e.g. 2.5×10^6 is the standard form way of writing 2500000. Many scientific calculators use standard form to show numbers too big (or too small) for their display, e.g. as 2.5 06.
Subset	Part of another set. See exercises 4A and 4B.
Sum	The result of an addition.

T

Tonne	A metric unit of mass, equal to 1000 kg. Little different to an imperial ton.
Topologically equivalent	See TOPOLOGY
Translation	The transformation of sliding. See TRANSLATION (25)

U

Union
'Joining together': see exercise 4D.

V

Vector
A line with both length and direction. See VECTORS (25)

Vertex
The correct name for a corner.

W

Whole number
An *integer*. 4 is a whole number, $5\frac{1}{2}$ is not.

Summaries: Book 1

Notes (a) Topics are given in alphabetical order.

(b) The numbers in brackets refer to chapters in *this* book (summarised on pages 230 to 234) where further information may be found.

Algebra (2, 12, 15)

Like terms have the same letters; they can be added and subtracted.

Examples $3x + 4x = 7x$

$2 + 2x + 3 = 5 + 2x$ (but you cannot add the 5 to the 2x as they are not like terms)

$5a - a + c = 4a + c$ (but you cannot add 4a to c as they are not like terms)

Notation Notation is the shorthand (or 'notes') way of writing statements.

The notation z^2 ('zed squared') means $z \times z$.

Using **algebraic notation**, $3 \times a \times b + 2 \times a$ would be written as $3ab + 2a$.

Angles (28) (See also Triangles)

Acute: less than 90°; **Obtuse**: between 90° and 180°; **Reflex**: more than 180°.

Approximations (23)

Approximate means 'roughly the same as'.

Remember Key figure 5 or more, round up.

Examples (a) 1365 → 1370 to the nearest ten (the tens' figure is 6, the key figure is the 5, so round 6 up to 7).

(b) 1365 → 1400 to the nearest hundred (the hundreds' figure is 3, the key figure is the 6, so round the 3 up to 4).

(c) 1365 → 1000 to the nearest thousand (the thousands' figure is 1, the key figure is the 3, so leave the 1 unchanged).

Circles (31)

Circumference is the name for a circle's perimeter.

An **arc** is part of the circumference.

The **diameter** is the longest possible **chord**. It passes through the **centre** and is twice as long as the **radius**.

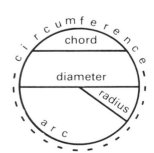

Fig. S1

S

Constructions (8)

The construction of a 60° angle is shown in Figure S2.

Fig. S2

Divisibility

Note: In all the following, divide ⇒ (implies) divides exactly a whole number of times.

Last figure: even ⇒ divides by 2; 0 ⇒ divides by 2, 5 and 10; 5 ⇒ divides by 5.

Digit-sum: 3, 6 or 9 ⇒ divides by 3 (and by 6 if an even number); 9 ⇒ divides by 9.

A number divides by 4 if the last two digits divide exactly by 4.

A number divides exactly by 8 if the last three digits divide exactly by 8.

Fibonacci's Sequence

1, 1, 2, 3, 5, 8, 13, etc.

Fractions (20)

You should be able to change common fractions to decimal fractions and vice versa.

Examples $\quad \dfrac{3}{5} \rightarrow 5\overline{)3.0}^{\,0.6} \qquad \therefore \text{(therefore) } \dfrac{3}{5} = 0.6$

$$0.6 = \frac{6}{10} = \frac{3}{5}; \qquad 0.65 = \frac{65}{100} = \frac{13}{20}; \qquad 0.654 = \frac{654}{1000} = \frac{327}{500}$$

Notes: When changing a decimal fraction to a common fraction:

10 at the bottom when the last figure is in the *tenths'* column.

100 at the bottom when the last figure is in the *hundredths'* column.

You should be able to multiply a fraction by an integer, with **cancelling**.

Examples $\quad \dfrac{{}^{2}8 \times 9^{3}}{{}_{13}\cancel{12}} = 6$

$$7\tfrac{3}{8} \times 12 \rightarrow \frac{59}{8} \times \cancel{12}^{3} = \frac{177}{2} = 88\tfrac{1}{2}$$

Note: Do not write the question as 59/8 × 12 or as $\tfrac{2}{3} \times 6$, but as $\dfrac{59 \times 12}{8}$ and $\dfrac{2 \times 6}{3}$.

Graphs (13)

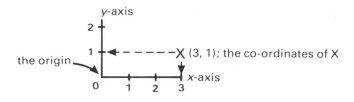

Fig. S3

Mappings (11)

A **mapping** changes one number to another by a given rule. The mapping arrow $\xrightarrow{\text{becomes}}$ is very useful when changing an expression into a different form, e.g. $1\frac{3}{4} \rightarrow \frac{7}{4}$; $17.89 \rightarrow 18$ correct to the nearest whole number.

Examples $x \rightarrow x - 3$ changes 12 into 9; 10 into 7; 8 into 5; etc.

{12, 10, 8} is called the **domain**.

{9, 7, 5} is called the **range**.

Mean (Average)

The **mean** (one of the three statistical averages but commonly just called 'the average') is found by dividing the total sum by the number of items.

Average speed is Total distance divided by Total time

Remember   Speed equals distance over time.

Metric System

Prefixes   **milli** $\Rightarrow \frac{1}{1000}$;   **centi** $\Rightarrow \frac{1}{100}$;   **kilo** $\Rightarrow 1000$

Note $\Rightarrow$ is the symbol for 'implies'

Length   1000 millimetres (1000 mm) = 1 metre (1 m)
100 centimetres (100 cm)   = 1 metre
1000 metres (1000 m)   = 1 kilometre (1 km)
Examples   28.5 mm = 2.85 cm
3.5 km = 3 km 500 m
3.05 km = 3 km 50 m

Weight   As for length, but based on the **kilogram** (kg). A gram ($\frac{1}{1000}$ kg) is a very small weight; two drawing pins weigh about 1 g.

The **tonne** is 1000 kg.

Capacity   The **litre** is the basic unit for liquid measure.

The centilitre and millilitre are in common use, but the term 'kilolitre' is not used.

Imperial equivalents

5 miles $\approx$ 8 kilometres ($\approx$ means 'is approximately')
1 foot $\approx$ 30 cm; 1 metre $\approx$ 39 inches
1 inch = 25.4 mm

1 pound $\approx$ 454 g; 100 g $\approx$ $3\frac{1}{2}$ ounces
1 stone $\approx$ $6\frac{1}{4}$ kg; 1 kg $\approx$ $2\frac{1}{4}$ lbs
1 ton $\approx$ 1 tonne

1 pint $\approx$ $\frac{1}{2}$ litre; 1 litre $\approx$ $1\frac{3}{4}$ pints
1 gallon $\approx$ $4\frac{1}{2}$ litres

Networks

Figure S4 shows a **network**.

The **nodes** are marked with large dots. The numbers give the orders of the nodes (the number of **arcs** that leave them).

This network has **4 regions** (remember the outside).

A corner with two arcs does not have to be a node; we have shown one that is and one that is not.

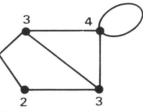

Fig. S4

Pascal's triangle

```
        1
       1 1
      1 2 1
     1 3 3 1
    1 4 6 4 1
      etc.
```

Percentage (29)

Percentage (%) means 'out of 100', so $35\% = \frac{35}{100} = \frac{7}{20}$.

To change a fraction to a percentage, multiply by 100%.

Examples $\frac{3}{5} \rightarrow \frac{3 \times 100\%}{5} \rightarrow \frac{3 \times \overset{20}{\cancel{100}}\%}{\underset{1}{\cancel{5}}} = 60\%$

$0.8 \rightarrow 0.8 \times 100\% = 80\%$

Polygons (22)

A **polygon** is a plane (flat) shape with straight-line sides.

Special names (number of sides in brackets): Triangle (3); Quadrilateral (4); Pentagon (5); Hexagon (6); Octagon (8); Decagon (10).

Convex

Concave

Fig. S5

Rectangle (22)

The area of a rectangle is its length multiplied by its width, or its base multiplied by its height.

Reflection

When you look into a mirror the image of yourself appears to be as far behind the mirror as you are in front of it.

In mathematical reflection we imagine ourselves to be looking down on the edge of the mirror, so that we can see both the object and the image, as shown in Figure S6.

The object (O) and the image (I) are the same distance from the mirror line, m, and the line joining them crosses m at right angles.

Hint: When drawing reflections it is much easier if the mirror is 'upright' on the page. Turn your paper if necessary.

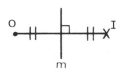

Fig. S6

Route Matrix

A route matrix describes a network; see Figure S7.

Note that the loop at C counts as *two* ways of going from C to C, clockwise and anticlockwise.

Sometimes the arcs are 'one-way', shown with arrows; see Figure S8.

		To		
		A	B	C
F	A	0	1	1
r	B	1	0	1
o				
m	C	1	1	2

Fig. S7

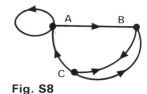

		To		
		A	B	C
F	A	1	1	0
r	B	0	0	1
o				
m	C	1	2	0

Fig. S8

Sets (4)

'**List a set**' means write all its **elements**.

'**Describe a set**' means write **what is special about the elements**.

$\in$ means '**is an element of**'

n( ) means '**the number of elements**'

Ø or { } is a **null set**, one with no elements.

Examples   Set A can be listed: $A = \{1, 3, 5, 7\}$

Set A can be described as 'The set of odd integers from 1 to 7'.

$5 \in A$ but $6 \notin A$

$n(A) = 4$.

Symmetry (line)

A **line (or axis) of symmetry** is best thought of as a fold line. Some examples are shown in Figure S9. Note that the parallelogram has no lines of symmetry; it will not fold in half.

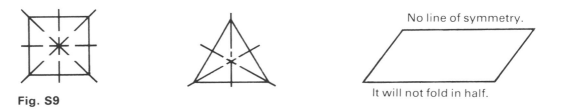

No line of symmetry.

It will not fold in half.

Fig. S9

Topology

Topology is the study of shapes that are distorted (stretched or shrunk) without changing: (a) the nodes or their orders; (b) the number of regions or their positions relative to each other; (c) the number of arcs.

Shapes thus distorted are said to be **topologically equivalent**; see Figure S10.

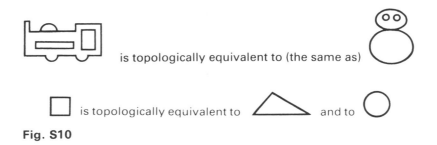

is topologically equivalent to (the same as)

is topologically equivalent to and to

Fig. S10

Triangles

The three angles of a triangle add up to 180°. This is called its '**angle sum**'. Some special triangles are shown in Figure S11.

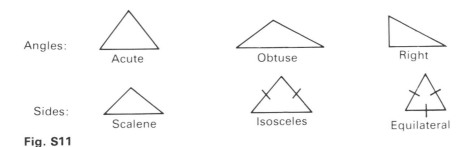

Angles: Acute   Obtuse   Right

Sides: Scalene   Isosceles   Equilateral

Fig. S11

Triangular number

A number that is part of the sequence:

1, 3, 6,   10 etc.

Note   Only 'key facts' are given in this summary. The numbers in brackets refer you to the book chapters, where fuller details will be found.

Bearings (1)

Three-figure bearings are measured clockwise from north (000°).

Cardinal bearings are stated in relation to the four cardinal points, north (N), east (E), south (S) and west (W).

Example   In Figure S12, point A is on the bearing south-west (SW) or 225° from point B.

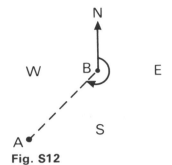

Fig. S12

Algebra (2, 12, 15)

Algebra is frequently revised in this course; look at the chapters given above and at the notes on page 223.

Be especially careful with $2b^2$, which means b^2 twice, **not** $2b$ squared.

Example   If $b = 3$ then $2b^2 = 2 \times 9 = 18$ (*not* $6^2 = 36$).

Negative integers/Directed numbers (3, 7, 9, 15)

Examples   If $a = -2$, $b = -3$, and $c = 4$:

(a) $a + b = -2 + -3 \to -2 - 3 = -5$ (Read $\to$ as 'becomes')

   Working $+ -3 \to -3$;
      $-2 - 3 \Rightarrow$ down 2, down 3 $\to$ down 5 $\to -5$. (Read $\Rightarrow$ as 'implies')

   Note $-2 - 3$ is not $+5$ as the -2 is not multiplied by -3. It is minus $\times$ minus, or minus minus, that makes a plus. It is **not** 'Two minuses make a plus'.

(b) $a - b = -2 - -3 \to -2 + 3 = 1$

   Working   Minus minus 3 makes plus 3;
      $-2 + 3 \Rightarrow$ down 2, up 3 $\to$ up 1 $\to 1$.

(c) $bc = -3 \times 4 = -12$

   Working   Down 3 four times $\to$ down 12 $\to -12$.

(d) $ab = -2 \times -3 = 6$

   Working   Minus multiplied by minus makes plus.

(e) $\dfrac{c}{a} = \dfrac{4}{-2} = -2$

   Working $\dfrac{c}{a} \Rightarrow c \div a = 4 \div -2$, or 'How many -2's make 4?'

(f) $\dfrac{a}{b} = \dfrac{-2}{-3} = \dfrac{2}{3}$

Working   Minus divided by minus makes plus.

Sets (4)

Chapter 4 introduces the terms **subset**, **intersection**, **union**, and **disjoint**.

Read the exercise introductions for revision notes.

Division by a decimal (5)

Unless using a calculator you must change the question so that you are dividing by an integer instead of a decimal.

See exercise 5C for examples.

Matrix addition (6)

A matrix displays information in a table. Matrices may be added if they are of the same order and the numbers in them refer to the same information.

See exercise 6B for examples.

Constructions (8)

You should be able to bisect angles; construct angles of 60°, 30°, 45° and 90°; construct a rectangle, a triangle given three sides, and the incircle and circumcircle of a triangle.

Chapter 8 gives examples of all these.

Area of a triangle (10)

The area of a triangle is half the base times the height.

Inequalities (11, 21)

See the introduction to exercise 11A, and exercise 21A, question 12.

Function notation (11)

$f:x \rightarrow 2x$ means 'A function of x such that x maps onto $2x$.'

A function is an event (like a wedding!); a mapping changes one value into another.

The function given above would change 4 into 8 and change 10 into 20.

Graphs (13)

Do not muddle the upright and horizontal lines.

In Figure S13, $x = 3$ goes through 3 on the x-axis.
$y = -2$ goes through -2 on the y-axis.

The hatched region is
$\{(x, y) : 0 < x < 3\} \cap \{(x, y) : -2 < y < 0\}$

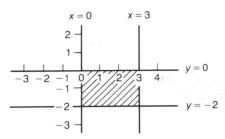

Fig. S13

Probability (16)

The probability of an event happening is given as a fraction between 0 (impossible) and 1 (certain).

This fraction is $\dfrac{\text{The number of ways the event can happen}}{\text{The total number of possible events}}$.

For examples see exercise 16B.

Pythagoras' Theorem (18)

The longest side of a right-angled triangle is called the **hypotenuse**.

The area of the square drawn on the hypotenuse is equal to the sum of the areas of the squares on the other two sides.

Ratio/Scales (19)

In Figure S14:

AB is divided at X in the ratio of 8 parts to 4 parts.

AX:XB = 8:4 = 2:1 (dividing both by 4).

If AX:XB = 2:1 then AX = 2XB.

In Figure S15:

CY:YD = 3:2, so CD is divided into 5 parts (3 + 2).

If CD is 15 cm then each part is $15 \div 5 = 3$ cm, so CY = 9 cm and YD = 6 cm,

A drawing to a scale of 1:30 has 1 unit of the drawing representing 30 units of the real object. A book 30 cm by 15 cm would be drawn 1 cm by $\frac{1}{2}$ cm on this scale.

Common fractions; addition/subtraction (20)

See chapter 20 for methods and examples.

Equation solution (21)

You should be able to solve equations where the letter-term only appears once by just thinking logically about the arithmetic of the equation. This is called 'solving by inspection'.

Chapter 21 explains a method that can be used to solve an equation when the letter-term appears more than once.

Special quadrilaterals (22)

If you draw accurate sketches you can easily observe the facts about the sides, angles and diagonals of the **kite, trapezium, isosceles trapezium, parallelogram, rectangle, rhombus,** and **square.** See the introduction to exercise 22A for diagrams of these special quadrilaterals.

It is especially important to remember:

The diagonals cross at right angles in the kite, the square and the rhombus.

The parallelogram has no lines of symmetry.

Note Strictly, the rectangle, rhombus and square are *all* parallelograms, but when we refer to 'a parallelogram' we are not referring to these *special* parallelograms.

Decimal place approximation (23)

See the introduction to exercise 23B.

Conversion graphs (24)

A conversion graph provides a rapid means of changing one quantity to another, e.g. °F to °C.

Vectors (25)

A vector is a line with length and direction.

Figure S16 illustrates the vector $\begin{pmatrix} 3 \\ 2 \end{pmatrix}$;

Figure S17 illustrates the vector $\begin{pmatrix} -3 \\ -2 \end{pmatrix}$.

Fig. S16

Fig. S17

The positive (+) and negative (−) directions are the same as for graph axes.

Translation (25)

A translation is a sliding movement.

The transformation of translation can be described by a vector.

In Figure S18 the vector $\begin{pmatrix} 3 \\ 1 \end{pmatrix}$ has **translated** the square, moving it 3 units forward and 1 unit up.

Fig. S18

Proportion (26)

For examples of the ratio method and the unitary method see the introduction to chapter 26.

Straight-line angles (28)

Adjacent; vertically opposite; corresponding; alternate; allied.

See the introductions to exercises 28A and 28B for examples of the above angles.

Percentages (29)

You should be able to find percentages of amounts, e.g. 15% of £25; 8% of 150.

When dealing with money it helps to remember that 1% of £1 is 1p.

See the introduction to exercise 29B for examples.

Circles (31)

You should be able to calculate the circumference of a circle given its radius or diameter, using the formula **Circumference equals π multiplied by diameter.**

Note   It is better to avoid the formula $C = 2\pi r$ as it is so easy to confuse it with the area formula $A = \pi r^2$.

Mode and median (32)

See the introductions to exercises 32A and 32B.

Cuboids and prisms (33)

You should be able to find the volume of a cuboid and a prism.

See the introductions to exercises 33A and 33B for examples.

Similar shapes (34)

Figure S19 shows a pair of similar shapes. They have sides in the ratio 1:2; that is, each side of the larger shape is twice the corresponding (in the same position) side of the smaller shape.

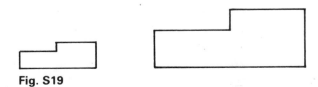

Fig. S19